Demons and Demonesses of Hindu Mythology

Priya Narayanan is a designer, writer, traveller, teacher and mother, not necessarily in that order. She runs her own design practice under the twin banners Tatva and Soma and is Professor at CEPT University, her alma mater. She is also a published poet and author. While her poems and short stories have appeared in various anthologies and literary magazines, she has four children's books under her belt and many more lurking in the deepest corners of her computer, waiting for their moment in the sun. When not practising and teaching design, she likes to travel solo and read everything that comes her way. You can learn more about Priya on her website, www.priyanarayanan.in

DEMONS AND DEMONESSES OF HINDU MYTHOLOGY

PRIYA NARAYANAN

RUPA

Published by
Rupa Publications India Pvt. Ltd 2021
7/16, Ansari Road, Daryaganj
New Delhi 110002

Sales centres:
Allahabad Bengaluru Chennai
Hyderabad Jaipur Kathmandu
Kolkata Mumbai

ISBN: 978-93-5520-036-5

First impression 2021

10 9 8 7 6 5 4 3 2 1

The moral right of the author has been asserted.

Printed at HT Media Ltd, Gr. Noida

For Amma,
who, for me, is the original teller of these tales

द्वौ भूतसर्गौ लोकेऽस्मिन्दैव आसुर एव च ।
दैवो विस्तरश: प्रोक्त आसुरं पार्थ मे शृणु ॥6॥

(Dvau bhūta-sargau loke 'smin daiva āsura eva cha
Daivo vistaraśhaḥ prokta āsuraṁpārtha me śhṛiṇu)

There are two kinds of beings in this world—those endowed
with a divine nature and those possessing a demoniac nature.
I have described the divine qualities in detail, O Arjun. Now
hear from me about the demoniac nature.

—*Bhagavad Gita*, Chapter 16, Verse 6

Contents

Introduction - BHU

Demons and demonesses are essentially supernatural beings who find themselves portrayed as evil wrong-doers in mythological stories and folklore from across the world. In Hindu mythology, they fall under the category of either asuras or rakshasas.

When I was young, I often heard my grandmother use the words 'asura-buddhi' and 'rakshasa-buddhi'. 'Buddhi' means intelligence and since you, my dear readers, are of the intelligent sort, I'm sure you can put two and two together to decipher what my grandmother was trying to say...or can you? After all, my own perception of the words has changed since I was a child.

Back then, asuras and rakshasas, at least according to the elders who surrounded me, meant only one thing—BIG, BAD, EVIL BEINGS (oh okay, I've listed three things, not one. My bad!). Not surprisingly, Grandmother used the aforementioned words to describe the intelligence of those with crooked or vile thoughts—be they the nasty people she encountered on bus and local train rides, or shopkeepers and vendors of the arguing variety or, of course, a select few from a species popularly known as politicians. I believed her then, because in all the bedtime stories Grandfather told me during the hot and sweaty summer holidays, the gods were good and the asuras or rakshasas were bad. It never occurred to me that I should question what counts as good and what as bad, so I gladly devoured the stories and nodded understandingly whenever Grandma said 'asura-buddhi', with a hint of contempt.

Now, of course, I think differently. Because the more I read about asuras and rakshasas, the more I'm convinced that not only were they powerful, magical and, at times exotic, they were also supremely intelligent. Who then, were these beings? Where did they come from? What drove them to be evil and wreak havoc everywhere they went? To know this, we'll have to travel back in time...no, not to my childhood, but way back to when the world was born.

I n the beginning, there was nothing but darkness. Then, Brahma, the creator of the universe, uttered three words. With 'bhūh', he generated the earth; with 'bhuvaha', he generated the air and with 'svaha', he generated the sky. He then set about populating the universe.

To help him with the task, Brahma gave birth to ten sons

Note 1

and a daughter. These children of Brahma were born out of his manasa or mind rather than body, and are hence called Manasaputras. Brahma then went on to create Daksha from his right thumb, Dharma from his chest, Kamadeva from his heart and Agni from his eyebrows. With this done, he finally created Manu as an image of himself.

Psst...this is something you better get used to. No being in the world of mythology is born the way you or I were born. You'll see what I mean when we get to the first story—it is sure to send your biology teacher into a tizzy! But hey, don't hop, skip and jump to the story as yet, there's much to be discovered before taking that plunge.

To get back to the story of creation, Brahma gave his daughter Shatarupa in marriage to Manu and it is their children who became the first Manavas or humans—our forefathers. At the same time, Rishi Kashyapa, one of Brahma's Manasaputras, was asked to marry thirteen of Daksha's several daughters. With them, he fathered the devas, gandharvas, danavas, daityas and part of the animal world, including fishes, birds, snakes and even some monsters. While the devas were born to his wife Aditi, the danavas and daityas, who were born to Danu and Diti, respectively, together make up the larger group that we know as asuras.

Rather simple and straightforward if we choose to ignore the part about having thirteen wives, and humans giving birth to birds and snakes, right? But the same cannot be said about the origin of rakshasas. Since rakshasas inhabited the earth, much like us humans, there have been several conjectures as to who they really were.

1. 10 sons + 1 daughter = 11 = 2 = duality. Daughter = Shatarupa

One account says that rakshasas were created from the breath of Brahma when he was asleep at the end of the Satya Yuga, or the Era of Truth. Soon after their creation, they were filled with a thirst for blood and started to eat Brahma himself. This prompted Brahma to shout 'Rakshama!' or 'Protect me!' following which, Vishnu came to his aid and banished all rakshasas to Earth.

According to another account, rakshasas are said to be the progeny of Rishi Pulastya, another of Brahma's Manasaputras. The story goes that Pulastya, who is also considered the forefather of yakshas, vanaras and kinnaras (beings with human-like bodies and horse-like heads), had two sons— Agastya and Visravas. When he came of age, Visravas married Rishi Bharadwaj's daughter Idvidaa and sired Kubera, the king of yakshas and God of Wealth. In the meantime, the daitya king Sumali was in search of a powerful being to marry his daughter Kaikeshi so that their descendants could become the undisputable rulers of the world. With Sumali already being the most powerful asura king, it was obvious that another asura would not qualify for the purpose, so he had to look elsewhere for his ideal son-in-law. But where could that be?

Even as Sumali was starting to get frustrated with his search, word reached him of Visravas's superior intellectual and yogic powers. Sumali immediately arranged for a chance encounter between his beautiful daughter and the sage, hoping they would fall in love. His ploy paid off. Soon, Kaikeshi and Visravas were married and they gave birth to three sons— Dashagriva (or Ravana), Kumbhkarna and Vibheeshana—and a daughter Meenakshi (or Shurpanakha), who became the *forest dwellers*

progenitors of all rakshasas to follow. Thus, rakshasas were the descendants of a mixed race of daityas and rishis. The greatest of them all, Ravana, was a daitya brahmana.

Phew! Did I just hear you heave a sigh of relief assuming that the mystery of the origin of rakshasas has been solved? Then you might want to take that breath back, my friend, for there's more to come.

One of the more interesting stories about the origin of rakshasas goes that when the first beings—Heti and Praheti—were created from Brahma's breath to inhabit the waters of the primordial ocean, they were not sure what the purpose of their lives was. After consultation with their creator, Heti decided that he would protect the waters and hence became a rakshaka (later corrupted to 'rakshasa'), while Praheti decided to worship the waters and became a yaksha (worshipper). It is said that after Brahma created all other beings, Heti married Bhaya, the sister of Yama, and had a son—Vidyutkesha, the grandfather of Sumali. Thus, as per this version, Sumali was a rakshasa, not a daitya. However, the story of his daughter marrying Visravas and begetting Ravana and his siblings remains the same.

There's one last conjecture about rakshasas and you might, perhaps, find this more believable since it has nothing to do with Brahma or sages or asuras. Some scholars believe that rakshasas were the Rakshaks or guardians of the forests. They lived in caves or under trees, ate fruits or animals and sustained on the resources the forest offered them. They also constantly roamed the forests and once in a while came in contact with humans during their wanderings. Humans, when confronted

NOTE

1. Could these be the subterranean, 'negative' ETs described in *Ancient Aliens*?

by beings who looked and acted so different from what they were used to, were almost always scared of the rakshasas and either ran away from them or prayed to them in the hope that they wouldn't be harmed. This is why we see that, even today, many villages have temples dedicated to rakshasas and people worship them as protectors of the village.

Now that you know where asuras and rakshasas came from, you might be wondering why they were considered BIG, BAD and EVIL. You might be surprised to know that in the earlier portions of the *Rig Veda*, which is the oldest Vedic text, the term 'asura' was used to describe all powerful beings with specialized knowledge and magical powers, irrespective of their nature. For instance, Indra, Varuna, Mitra and Agni, some of the key Vedic deities, have been frequently addressed as 'asura' in these verses. However, as the remaining portions of the *Rig Veda* were being written, it seems as though the writers felt a need to separate the good from the evil. But how?

Some scholars think that the answer lies in understanding the term 'sura'. According to them, 'sura' comes from 'Surya', the supreme Vedic god, and is thus any being who radiates with light and knows his real Self or Aatman, which leads to contentment and happiness. As against this, asura is one who does not know the Aatman and is hence full of desires that lead to greed, discontent, envy and other evil thoughts. Since the term 'deva' means 'light' or 'to shine', the authors of the Vedas wrote about 'asuras who became devas' by choosing to use their power and knowledge for constructive or positive purposes and 'asuras who remained asuras' by choosing to use the same for destructive purposes.

Thus, the only thing that differentiated a deva from an asura was intent, action and the choices they made in their lives. Consequently, Indra, Soma, Agni, Vayu and several other Vedic deities came to be considered as devas while all the danavas and daityas were labelled as asuras. This interpretation of asura only grew with time, and by the time some of the important Puranas were written, its meaning had completely changed from that of a 'powerful being' to a 'wicked or evil being'.

Similarly, it was only in the Ramayana and later, the Mahabharata, that rakshasas were first shown to be purposeful troublemakers. These epics portrayed rakshasas and rakshasis as hideous beings with magical powers—they could fly, spit fire and retain poison within their bodies without being affected by it. Their most important magical power, of course, was that of illusion. They were remarkable shapeshifters, able to change size and take on any form they wished to, conning both humans and human incarnations of gods in the process. Because of these powers, you will find that in stories from the Ramayana and the Mahabharata, rakshasas and rakshasis were often called upon by their own leaders or other asura kings to create unrest among humans, especially sages who conducted yagnas (sacrificial rituals) to appease the gods.

With that, dear readers, we have come to the end of this section. However, before we move on, here's some trivia about the key differences between asuras and rakshasas.

(1)   ◆ Asuras had been banished to reside in Patalaloka, while rakshasas lived on the earth, amongst humans.

Brd point 3!! ; *danavas* 3 *daityas*

(2)
- ◆ Asuras matched the devas in supernatural powers and were always at war with them, vying for Devaloka and attempting to dethrone Indra and the other devas. They had an unquenchable thirst for what was not theirs; greed and pride were the key attributes that drove them to their downfall. On the other hand, rakshasas were less intelligent and powerful compared to the devas and were troublemakers in the human world.

(3)
- ◆ Asuras always challenged the authority of Vishnu, Shiva and Goddess Shakti. Consequently, they did torturous penances or tapas to get boons—ranging from immortality to cleverly choosing when, where, how, and by whom they could be killed. Many rakshasas, however, were born thus due to some curse or the other. For instance, the arrogance of a deva, gandharva, apsara or even a human king could result in him/her being cursed by an irate sage to be born as a rakshasa or rakshasi with a caveat that they would be able to return to their original form if they had the good luck of being killed by a human incarnation of Vishnu.

We now know who the asuras and rakshasas were. Before we plunge into their stories though, there is one more aspect we should know: where did these demons reside? Rakshasas, as we already saw, cohabited the earth with humans, while the danavas and daityas lived in Patalaloka, or the netherworld. But where was this Patalaloka and what did it look like? Was

Mantra from Rig Veda; 6+1 (1+6)

it a horrible hellish place considering the asuras were always trying to capture the resplendent Devaloka and rule over it? Let's find out...

Bila Swarga

According to the Vedas, the universe is divided into three distinct parts: the Urdhvaloka (highest abodes whose residents are super-intelligent, superhuman, semi-divine and spiritually advanced beings), Madhyaloka (middle abodes that comprise the earth, as we know it, along with six other island worlds whose residents are far more advanced—intellectually and materially—than humans and live longer lives) and Adholoka (lower realms where the residents are supremely powerful and intelligent but are more inclined to worldly pleasures than spiritual growth).

ॐ भू:, ॐ भुव:, ॐ स्व:, ॐ मह:
ॐ जन:, ॐ तप:, ॐ सत्यम

(Om Bhuh, Om Bhuvaha, Om Swaha, Om Mahaha,
Om Janaha, Om Tapaha, Om Satyam)

If you're wondering why we're chanting a mantra all of a sudden, rest assured there is a connection. This mantra from the *Rig Veda* is essentially a reflection of the map of Urdhvaloka. Of these, Bhuh refers to Bhuloka. When you start moving upwards from here, you encounter the six worlds of Bhuvarloka, Svarloka, Maharloka, Tapaloka, Janaloka and finally Satyaloka, which is the world of Brahma. Svarloka is the world that we know as Swarga or Devaloka, where the thirty-three devas resided along with the gandharvas and apsaras and were ruled by Indra from the capital city of Amaravati. Bhuvarloka is the realm of the sun, moon and planets as well as highly intelligent beings such as the Sapta Rishis, Siddhas, Charanas and Vidyadharas.

Coming back to Bhuloka, it comprised seven concentric oceans (*sagara*) alternating with seven concentric islands (*dvipa*). At the centre of Bhuloka is Mount Meru (or Sumeru Parvata) and immediately surrounding it is Jambudvipa, which is the earth as we know it. Meru, also called the King of Mountains in the scriptures, is the support of Jambudvipa on the fringes of which lies the Lavana Sagara or the Salty Ocean. The other rings, growing bigger and bigger like ripples in the water as we leave the centre, are Plakshadvipa surrounded by the Ikshu Sagara (Ocean of Sugarcane Juice), Shalamlidvipa surrounded by the Sura Sagara (Ocean of Wine), Kushadvipa surrounded by the Sarpis Sagara (Ocean of Ghee), Kraunchadvipa surrounded by the Ksheera Sagara (Ocean of Milk), Shakadvipa surrounded by the Dadhi Sagara (Ocean of Yogurt) and finally Pushkaradvipa surrounded by the Jala Sagara (Ocean of Clear Water).

Phew, that was a mouthful of dvipas and sagaras, wasn't it? But wait, there's one more ocean that we need to know about...one which, unlike the above-mentioned ones that constitute the living world, lies farther below Adholoka. This is the Garbhodaka Ocean or the cosmic ocean—the basis of the entire universe, just as the womb is the basis for the creation of life. The water in this ocean, where Vishnu rests

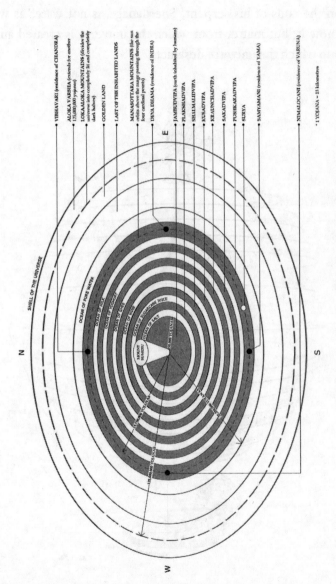

N

E

S

W

SHELL OF THE UNIVERSE

OCEAN OF PURE WATER

OCEAN OF MILK

OCEAN OF LIQUOR

OCEAN OF GHEE

OCEAN OF CURD

OCEAN OF SUGARCANE JUICE

OCEAN OF SALT

OCEAN ARMY

MOUNT SUMERU

VIBHAVARI (residence of CHANDRA)

ALOKA VARSHA (extends for another 125,000,000 yojanas)

LOKAALOKA MOUNTAINS (divides the universe into completely lit and completely dark halves)

GOLDEN LAND

LAST OF THE INHABITED LANDS

MANASOTTARA MOUNTAINS (the sun orbits above the range passing through the four cardinal points)

DEVA DHAMA (residence of INDRA)

JAMBUDVIPA (earth inhabited by humans)

PLAKSHADVIPA

SHALMALIDVIPA

KUSADVIPA

KRAUNCHADVIPA

SAKADVIPA

PUSHKARADVIPA

SURYA

SAMYAMANI (residence of YAMA)

NIMALOCANI (residence of VARUNA)

* 1 YOJANA = 13 kilometres

Bhumandala, or the Structure of Bhuloka

on the coils of his serpent, Sheshanaga, is not water as we know it, but matter from which the universe is created and into which the universe destructs.

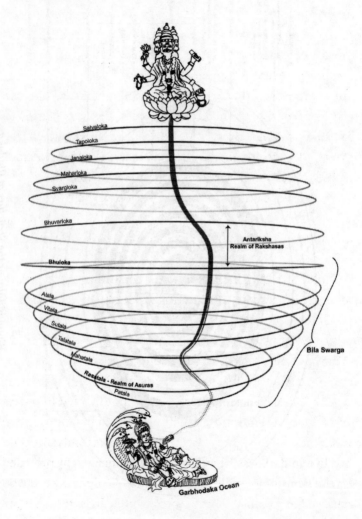

Structure of the Vedic Universe

Between Bhuvarloka and Bhuloka is Antariksha, which is essentially a vast expanse of space. While the yakshas and rakshasas reside on Bhuloka, they also have access to Antariksha owing to the great magical powers they wield.

Now, below Bhuloka too lies a Swargaloka, but this is Swarga of a different kind. Called Bila Swarga, this region comprises seven worlds moving downwards from Bhuloka. These are Atala, Vitala, Sutala, Talatala, Mahatala, Rasatala and Patala and combined together, they are also referred to as Adholoka, or more commonly, Patalaloka. Here is where you will find the abode of the great daitya and danava kings whose stories you will read in the following pages.

A word of caution here: Patalaloka is not to be confused with Naraka or hell. While the latter is not a nice place to find yourself in, you might just enjoy a trip to Patala ! Here's why.

Bila Swarga, created by the demon architect Maya to replicate Swarga, affords its residents all the material pleasures one could wish for—fantastic architecture, perfectly manicured gardens with flowering plants, lakes and exquisite birds, a pleasant atmosphere throughout the year, and juices and elixirs that keep them free from disease or signs of physical ageing. Here, time is not divided into days and nights and since no sunlight reaches these worlds, there is darkness all the time. However, the danavas and daityas do not live in darkness; they live in the artificial light provided by the gemstones embedded in the hoods of the Nagas, who are also the co-inhabitants of these worlds. In fact, such is the dazzling brightness of the light from these gems that there is practically no dark spot in all of Patala!

Thus, in essence, the asuras enjoy all the material luxuries of life just like the devas. The only difference is that asuras are mortal while devas are not...and therein lies the root of all the great battles waged between these group of supposed half-brothers!

NOTE

Now that we know all there is to know about asuras and rakshasas, let us get under their skin and find out what it means to be one of them. As is true with all knowledge passed down by word of mouth from one generation to another, the stories of these demons and their origin are varied and subject to interpretations. While one account may say one thing about a particular demon, another might add or subtract, even distort a few aspects for the benefit of the audience it was being told to.

Many a time, the difference is not so much in the life story of the demon as it is in the notion of who killed him—was it Vishnu, Shiva or Devi?

My research has led me to believe that the ancient texts have been interpreted differently by followers of different gods. For instance, followers of Devi attribute the slaying (or at least creating the circumstances for the slaying) of an asura to the different incarnations of Devi. In their versions of a story, you will see Brahma, Vishnu or Shiva praying to Devi to help them accomplish the feat, thus establishing her superiority. The same holds true for versions created by the

1. Can Asuras become inorganic beings? (a la Captaye da)

followers of Vishnu and Shiva.

In the following pages, you'll read the stories of some of the most intriguing demons and demonesses of Hindu mythology—from Mahishasura and the infamous ten-headed Ravana, to lesser-known demons such as Jalandhara, the five-headed Mura and the headless Kabandha.

So, what are you waiting for? Turn the page and dive right into the Garbhodaka Ocean, where it all started...

1

Madhu and Kaitabha

*Much before Brahma started the process of creation,
whereby he created both devas and asuras, two demons
were born into the universe and being born, they lived
for thousands of years before they died. Who were these
demons? And if Brahma did not create them, how were
they born?*

❖

Long before the world was created, when there was no
heaven, no earth, no day and no night, the universe
was only a vast ocean. In the middle of this ocean,
Narayana (one who rests on the waters of creation) rested in

a deep meditative state, on the coils of Aadishehsa, the Great Snake. As nothing had yet been created, there was nothing to preserve or look after; so, Narayana remained in this trance for thousands of years until a lotus suddenly sprung out from his navel and bloomed. Inside this lotus was Brahma, reciting the Vedas. But, with Goddess Aadyashakti (the first and most supreme power), residing within him in the form of Yoganidra (a deep state of meditation), Narayana slept on and on, oblivious to everything.

Once, two specks of ear wax fell from Narayana's ear into the sea and out of these specks emerged a pair of beings.

'Who are we? Where are we? How did we come here?' they wondered as they swam in the deep waters of the cosmic ocean. Then, noticing something far above them, they swam upwards. 'Who is this giant?' they wondered, swimming around Aadishesha.

As they searched for answers to their questions, Goddess Aadyashakti appeared before them.

'I know you have many questions; it is time I answered them for you,' she said. Then, conferring them with the names Madhu and Kaitabha, she taught them the mantra that explained the origin of the universe and vanished into nothingness.

Wonderstruck, the two beings recited the mantra and worshipped Aadyashakti for a thousand years until she reappeared in front of them.

'You have been born into this universe, so one day you will have to die; that is the cycle of life,' the Goddess said. 'However, you have pleased me with your devotion, so I grant you the boon that when the time comes, you will have the power to choose how you die.'

Even as the Goddess's image faded away, Madhu wondered, 'What did she mean by giving us the power to choose how to die? Why would we choose to die at all!'

'Yes, why would we indeed?' repeated Kaitabha. Then, with a sudden brightness flooding his face, Kaitabha said, 'Do you know what it means? It means we are immortal. We shall never choose to die, so we shall never die.'

The thought made the beings very happy. Soon, they mastered the art of walking on and under the waters and explored every nook of the ocean until one day, they returned to where Narayana lay with his eyes shut. Looking up, they saw Brahma, also deep in meditation in his lotus as he prepared for the next phase of creation. The intense light emanating from his hands lured Madhu and Kaitabha.

'Who are these beings? And what is that brilliant light?' they wondered. Climbing up the lotus, they found the Vedas shining like gemstones in Brahma's hands and were immediately enchanted.

'I don't know what these are, but they must be something precious. Let's take them with us,' said Madhu. And so, they stole the Vedas and fled to hide in the deep recesses of the ocean.

Upon opening his eyes, Brahma was deeply upset to find his Vedas missing. He plunged into the ocean in search of them and finally reached Madhu and Kaitabha's hideout, but when he requested them to return the scriptures, they attacked him and scared him away.

Distressed, Brahma prayed to Aadyashakti. 'O great Goddess, the Vedas are my eyes and they have been taken away from me! Without them, I cannot create the rest of the universe. Please ask Yoganidra to leave Narayana, so he can wake up and retrieve them for me.'

Sympathizing with Brahma's plight, the Goddess withdrew her power of Yoganidra. Narayana woke up from his slumber and, assuming the name Vishnu (he who pervades everywhere), he dived into the ocean to fight Madhu and Kaitabha. However, he could not defeat the duo even after battling them for several thousands of years. As he wondered what tactic he should use next, Goddess Aadyashakti appeared before him.

'Remember, O Vishnu, that Madhu and Kaitabha are born from a part of you,' she said. 'They possess all your strengths and cannot be killed unless they themselves disclose the manner in which they want to die. If you want to defeat them, you must use the power of trickery rather than physical strength. And I shall help you with my power of Maya (illusion).'

Vishnu thought about the Goddess's words for some time. He then went to Madhu and Kaitabha and pretended to lay down his arms.

'O great warriors, I have been fighting for thousands of years but have not been able to defeat you. You are indeed the mightiest of all. I bow down to you,' Vishnu said.

The two demons smiled triumphantly. There were only two other beings in their universe apart from them. Brahma, they had already terrorized and scared away; now Vishnu too had submitted to their superiority!

Even as they rejoiced in the illusion of their victory, Vishnu interrupted, 'However, you must know that I am the Supreme Being in this universe. Since you have defeated me, I shall grant you whatever boon you wish for. So, ask for anything you want and it shall be yours!'

The proclamation by Vishnu irked Madhu and Kaitabha. 'How dare a being whom we have vanquished declare himself to be the Supreme Being! How dare he think of granting us a boon!' they conferred with each other.

Then, turning to Vishnu, they laughed in arrogance and said, 'O wretched being, it is us who are supreme, not you! Did you not just agree that we defeated you? But we will not hold your words against you; instead, now that we are superior to you in every way, it is us who should be granting the boon. So, tell us what boon you want and you shall have it!'

Vishnu smiled. 'In that case, my lords, please grant me the boon that I can kill you,' he said.

Vishnu's words took the demons by surprise; in fact, it rattled them. But they had offered to grant the boon and now, there was no way they could take back their words. As Madhu and Kaitabha looked at each other, it dawned upon them that they were, after all, mortal—as Goddess Aadyashakti had said. However, they still had the power to choose how they would die. What if they came up with an impossible condition? Wouldn't it make them immortal again?

After thinking for a long time, they finally said, 'So be it. You may kill us, but you can do so only in a dry place; find a place that is not submerged under this water that surrounds us and your boon shall be granted.'

Vishnu glanced all around. The universe had only water in it, nothing else. The demons had chosen the condition of their death wisely, but there had to be a way to slay them. Then, even as Madhu and Kaitabha looked on, thinking that they had outwitted him, Vishnu raised his thighs and expanded them until they reached far above the surface of the water. Alarmed, the demons also enlarged their bodies to the extent of a thousand yojanas, but Vishnu expanded his thighs further so that they became a dry island floating on the ocean waters of the universe. Then, catching hold of the demons, he laid them on his thighs and cut off their heads with his discus.

When their heads were severed from their bodies, the vast surface of the ocean was covered with the Medas (fat) of the demons. It is said that that this Medas collected itself into a lump and became the earth, thus giving the earth its alternative name, Medini.

Note

A yojana is a Vedic measurement of length and roughly equals 13 kilometres.

You would have noticed that at the beginning of the story, Madhu and Kaitabha were just two 'beings', they weren't born as demons. However, the changes that came upon them and their actions after receiving the boon from Aadyashakti, made them arrogant, proud, greedy and conceitful. Hence, they became demons and are considered the first 'asuric' forces in the universe despite being born from Vishnu himself.

In Sanskrit, Madhu means 'honey' while Kaitabha means 'insect-like'. Put together, scholars have interpreted Madhu-Kaitabha to mean 'similar to honeybees,' thus symbolizing the lives of those who work hard, like honeybees, to accumulate honey or material comforts, but do not use their intellect to think about the higher things in life. As per another interpretation, Madhu is a metaphor for 'honeyed praise', while Kaitabha symbolizes 'sour criticism'. Both enter our mind through our ears and are equally destructive to our intellect, which is symbolized by Brahma.

2

Hiranyaksha

Madhu and Kaitabha were the first asuric forces in the universe. However, they weren't created by Brahma, but were born involuntarily from Vishnu's ears. After they were slain by their own creator and the Vedas restored to Brahma, the latter started the process of creation in earnest and soon, along with the devas, the first daityas were born into the universe, heralding a never-ending battle between the 'good' and 'bad', 'right' and 'wrong'. Do you know who they were?

✤

When the daitya twins Hiranyaksha and Hiranyakashipu were born to Kashyapa and his wife Diti, the entire universe trembled in fear. As though foreseeing her fate, volcanoes erupted all around Bhumi; strong winds howled as thunderstorms and cyclones enveloped her and gigantic waves surged across the seas. With jackals and dogs howling through the days and nights, with animals running hither and thither as though possessed, with birds shrieking in their nests and cows, in their fear, yielding blood instead of milk, it seemed as if the world was nearing its end.

Even as Bhumi struggled to return to her original state of peace and equilibrium, the twins grew up rapidly. Soon, they were taller than the tallest mountains with the crests of their dazzling crowns touching the sky and blocking the sun. Their bodies were as hard as steel and with each of their strides, the earth shook and quaked. When they were old enough to be crowned kings, the brothers set their sights on conquering the three worlds of Patala, Bhuloka and Swarga. However, as they gathered a large army of asuras and prepared to fight the devas, Hiranyaksha and Hiranyakashipu realized that achieving their goal in itself wasn't enough; what good would all the effort be if they couldn't remain alive forever to enjoy the fruits of their battles? So, leaving their kingdom, they went deep into the forests to do severe tapas (penance) and pray to Brahma in the hope that they would be granted immortality.

'Open your eyes, O great devotees of mine,' Brahma said when he appeared before them after thousands of years of penance. 'Ask for a boon each and it shall be granted.'

Both Hiranyaksha and Hiranyakashipu wished to be granted immortality, but explaining the inevitability of death, Brahma asked them to choose instead the condition under which they would want to die.

'Then let no man, animal or God be able to kill me,' asked Hiranyaksha.

'Grant me that the being that would kill me would be neither man nor God nor animal, the time of my death would be neither day nor night, the place of my death would be neither in heaven nor on earth, neither inside nor outside my house,' said Hiranyakashipu, smiling to himself for having covered all possibilities of him ever getting killed. Then, pausing to think for a while, he added, 'Also, O Brahma, grant me that I cannot be killed with a weapon.'

Brahma smiled and granted the wishes to the brothers, who, assured of their immortality, unleashed a reign of terror on the three worlds. With boons that meant even the gods couldn't kill them, they commanded every being in the universe to worship only them and no one else.

However, despite their orders, the sages on earth continued to worship Shiva, Vishnu and Devi and offered oblations to the devas during their yagnas. When this was brought to Hiranyaksha's notice, he was beyond himself with anger.

'How dare you disobey me!' he thundered at the sages, disrupting their yagnas. 'Your impudence will cost you dearly; just wait and watch,' he declared, and even as the entire universe looked on, Hiranyaksha dislodged Bhumi from her axis and dropped her deep into Ksheera Sagara.

As Bhumi sank towards Patala, Brahma was distraught. There was no place for his creations to live on and hence, there was no meaning in creating. The devas, who drew their strength through the yagnas performed by the sages, started becoming weaker. Pleased with the chaos he had unleashed, Hiranyaksha kept Bhumi hidden in the ocean bed and returned to torment the devas, knowing that their strength was waning.

The devas, along with Brahma, approached Vishnu for help.

'O Vishnu, you are the only one who can deliver us from the tortures of Hiranyaksha,' pleaded Brahma. 'He has hidden Bhumi away and without her, neither can I create any more nor can the devas retain their strength!'

'O Brahma, you have granted Hiranyaksha the boon that he cannot be killed by any man, animal or God. It is not in my capacity to slay him,' Vishnu replied.

Brahma nodded in melancholy. 'Everyone who prays to me and appeases me with their penance expects to be granted immortality. While I am bound by their devotion to give them what they seek, I tell them that no one is exempt from the cycle of life and death and ask them to choose a condition under which they would like to die or be killed. O Vishnu, it is true that Hiranyaksha asked not to be killed by an animal, but amongst all the animals that he named, he forgot to mention the boar. So, I pray to you, take the form of a boar and kill him so Bhumi can be free again.'

Vishnu smiled. 'So be it,' he said and went back to his deep meditative state.

Reassured, Brahma too went back to his meditation.

Soon, a tiny boar, Varaha, not larger than the tip of a thumb, emerged from Brahma's nostrils and grew larger and larger until he was over six thousand yojanas in height. Even as the devas looked on, Varaha let out a mighty roar and dived into Ksheera Sagara in search of Bhumi. Finding her languishing in the deepest recesses of the ocean, he used his tusks to dig her out of the ocean bed. Then, balancing her between his tusks, he started to rise towards the surface.

In the meantime, having defeated the devas and driven them out of Devaloka, Hiranyaksha had reached Nimalocani, the capital of the Ocean God Varuna. There, in the presence of Varuna's courtiers, he mocked him with snide remarks about his valour.

'O Varuna, you have conquered all the daityas and danavas in the universe, you have performed the great Rajasuya sacrifice, will you not accept my humble challenge and fight me?' he taunted.

Hiranyaksha's words pierced Varuna's pride, but he knew well enough that he was no match for the mighty asura. So, instead of accepting the challenge, he said, 'O Hiranyaksha, I do not need to fight you to know that you are more powerful than me. This I know already. But I also know that there is someone who matches you in strength and power...and most certainly surpasses you on both counts; and that is Vishnu.'

His ego hurt, Hiranyaksha seethed with rage. 'Where is this Vishnu?' he wondered to himself. 'I must find and fight him so that the matter of my superiority is settled once and for all!'

As he set out to seek his rival, Hiranyaksha came upon

Narada. 'Have you seen Vishnu?' he asked the sage haughtily.

'Yes indeed!' replied Narada. 'Didn't you know? Vishnu is busy carrying away Bhumi, who you had kept hidden all this while. Does it mean he has won this round of the battle?'

Stung by Narada's words, Hiranyaksha roared and dived into the ocean in search of Vishnu, but when he intercepted Varaha carrying Bhumi on his tusks, he started to laugh at the incredulity of the sight in front of him.

'So the lord of the universe, the great Vishnu, is a wild boar?' he sneered. 'Well, if the three worlds have only you to protect them, I can only pity them for I wonder what they would do when I smash your head into pieces!'

Despite the taunts, Varaha ignored Hiranyksha and kept rising until he reached the surface of the ocean and settled Bhumi on her axis again.

Irked with his rival's impudence, Hiranyaksha rushed towards Varaha with his mace. 'I have conquered Bhumi with my might, who are you to take her away? If you want her, you will have to defeat me in battle!' he thundered.

Now that Bhumi was safe, Varaha turned to fight Hiranyaksha. Seeing the asura hurl his mace towards him, Varaha stepped aside with a calmness that annoyed his rival. Picking up his mace again, Hiranyaksha brandished it and attacked Varaha a second time, successfully averting a blow to his own face. Thus, the two supremely powerful beings fought for a thousand years, with each matching the other in strength in the use of magical weapons and in their powers of illusion.

Once during the battle, Hiranyaksha's strike caused

Varaha to lose his mace. The asura king, however, refused to take advantage of the situation, for despite his anger and ego, he respected the code of war that forbade one from attacking an unarmed enemy. Varaha smiled in appreciation, but to him, the battleground was no place for concessions. Bereft of his mace, he invoked his discus—the Sudarshana Chakra, and resumed the fight. Hiranyaksha, an expert with the mace, manoeuvred and hurled it at Varaha several times with the force of a tempest. However, the mace could not find its target; at times, Varaha dodged it efficiently and at times, he deftly caught it in his hands and hurled it back at Hiranyaksha. As the fight continued, the mace finally fell close to Varaha's feet.

'Come, pick it up and try again,' Varaha mocked his rival, knowing well that Hiranyaksha would not bend to touch his feet.

Frustrated and humiliated, Hiranyaksha refused to take back the mace. Instead, with eyes burning like fire, he picked up a trident and threw it towards Varaha. The shiny weapon was however shattered to pieces by the Sudarshana Chakra. Infuriated, Hiranyaksha rushed towards Varaha and struck his chest hard with his fist. He then suddenly disappeared from sight.

Just as suddenly, fierce winds started to blow in from all directions, whipping up dust and blinding Varaha. Thunder and lightning filled the skies but instead of rain, what fell from the clouds were stones, blood and bones. Soon, Varaha found himself facing a deluge of weapons from all directions, even as demons and demonesses armed with tridents, their hair hanging loose and eyes spouting fire, assailed him. Finding himself surrounded by the magical powers of Hiranyaksha, Varaha closed his eyes and sent forth his Chakra to annihilate everything that came in its path.

Seeing his magical creations laid to waste, Hiranyaksha reappeared on the battlefield and embraced Varaha with all his might, hoping to crush him to death. His rival was too strong for him though and before he knew it, Varaha pushed him away and gored him to death with his tusks.

Note

The oblations offered to the gods during a yagna are known as Havis, which is usually poured into the sacred fire. It is said that Agni acts as the messenger and takes them up to the gods in the form of smoke. The devas need these offerings to maintain their power; they become weaker and weaker when mortals stop offering sacrifices. For this reason, whenever an asura becomes all-powerful, his first act is to disrupt the yagnas performed by the sages, and cut the devas off from the Havis.

Several years after slaying Hiranyaksha, Vishnu took the form of Narasimha to kill Hiranyakashipu. In Sanskrit, 'Hiranyaksha' means 'one with golden eyes' and 'Hiranyakashipu' means 'one who is clothed in gold'. Scholars have interpreted the former to mean 'one with an eye for gold' and hence, the twins themselves, to represent the tendency to hoard and dwell in luxury. The idea that Vishnu had to reincarnate twice to slay the brothers separately has been inferred to show that while it is possible to destroy lust or anger with a single blow, greed is a more formidable rival that requires greater willpower and discipline to vanquish.

3

Hayagriva

You must have heard the proverbs 'only a diamond can cut a diamond' or 'you need a thief to catch a thief'; but have you heard of 'you need a Hayagriva to slay a Hayagriva'? If not, plunge right into this story to find out what it means.

'Om Kamakshi Namaha. Om Kamadayini Namaha. Om Bhadra Priyaya Namaha. Om Paarvatye Namaha...' Hayagriva's ceaseless chants in praise of Shakti, the Supreme Goddess, reverberated through the world for a hundred years.

Born to Sage Kashyap and Devi Danu, Hayagriva was a terrifying asura with the head of a horse. ('Haya' translates to 'horse' and 'griva' translates to 'neck', but when put together, the word 'Hayagriva' means 'one with the head of a horse'.) Although he had been accepted as the king of all asuras, he thirsted for more. He wanted to be the ruler of the three worlds and for that, he would have to be invincible. So, he left the comforts of his palace to go high up in the mountains, where there was nothing but the harsh sun and the merciless winds for company.

Standing on one leg and with arms raised above his head in prayer, Hayagriva meditated upon the thousand names of Devi Bhagawati year after year without eating a morsel of food or drinking a drop of water. Pleased with his unstinted devotion, Devi finally appeared before him and offered to grant a boon.

'O Devi! Grant me the boon of invincibility and that if I should ever die, it should be only at the hands of another Hayagriva, i.e., a being with the head of a horse.'

'So be it!' said Devi with a smile before she disappeared.

Hayagriva then returned to his kingdom and started preparations to go to war with the devas. Gathering the might of all asura kings, he laid siege on Devaloka. The hapless devas rushed to Vishnu and asked him to fight for them. Vishnu agreed and thus followed a long and ferocious battle between him and Hayagriva even as the devas and asuras clashed amongst each other. However, with the boon of invincibility, Hayagriva was able to match every strategy used by Vishnu. A fight that the devas had thought would end in a few days continued for years on end until finally, Vishnu left for his abode, Vaikuntha.

The battle had taken its toll on Vishnu and he needed to recuperate and replenish his strength. So, Vishnu sat in Padmasana with his head resting on the upper end of Sharanga, his bow, and went into a deep state of meditation called Yoganidra.

Seeing this, the devas were distressed. They would surely lose the battle and Devaloka to Hayagriva if Vishnu did not go back to fight with them. They prayed to Brahma, who devised a plan to arouse Vishnu from his meditative sleep. Creating a termite, he sent it to gnaw at Vishnu's bowstring.

'When the string breaks, the resonant sound it will create will surely wake him up!' said Brahma to the devas.

As predicted, when the termite bit the fore-end of the Sharanga, the tight string gave way, sending a horrifying sound reverberating through the universe. Almost immediately, the earth quaked and mountains trembled, the waters of the ocean rose high and the sun lost its way. When the devas looked to see if the sound had woken Vishnu up, a gory sight confronted them. In front of them was the headless torso of Vishnu, still sitting in Padmasana. The force with which the bow-string snapped had severed Vishnu's head and sent it flying into the deep waters of Lavana Sagar, leaving behind no trace.

The devas stared at each other in disbelief and Brahma trembled in his seat. What could be more calamitous than the beheading of the very preserver of the universe?

'We must pray to the Supreme Goddess,' a mortified

Brahma told the devas. 'She is the life force behind the universe; only she can show us the way!' So saying, he started to pray to the Goddess, singing her praises along with the devas.

When Devi appeared before them, Brahma bowed and lamented, 'What have I done, Devi! I'm afraid I will be the cause of the end of this universe, now that Vishnu himself is no more!'

'Do not worry,' said the Goddess, 'nothing can happen to Vishnu, for he is indestructible. Everything that happens, does so for a cause, so go, find the head of a horse and attach it to Vishnu's neck. This way, he will become a Hayagriva and will be able to slay the asura who goes by the same name. Emboldened by my boon, he has oppressed the world for a long time. The time has now come for Vishnu to slay him.'

Bowing to the Supreme Goddess, the devas lost no time in hunting down a white horse and attaching its head to Vishnu's torso. Thus revived and revitalized, Vishnu went back to war with Hayagriva.

Upon seeing his nemesis in the form of a horse-headed being, Hayagriva was astonished. He had not expected another being such as himself to be born in all of the three worlds! At once, he realized the reason for Devi's smile when she granted him his boon. No matter what improbable condition one sets for one's death, death eventually catches up; every being that is born in this universe will ultimately have to die. Nevertheless, Hayagriva let out a thunderous roar and invited Vishnu to fight him, for that was his destiny.

In the battle that ensued, the horse-headed Vishnu smote Hayagriva with his mace and killed him.

Note

According to another version of the story, the asura Hayagriva stole the Vedas after receiving his boon and Vishnu, taking the form of a Hayagriva, kills him and restores the Vedas to Brahma. Asura here is, hence, a metaphor for the clutches of ignorance from which wisdom needs to be retrieved and restored. Yet another version says that the demon Hayagriva was killed by Vishnu's incarnation as a fish—the Matsya Avatara.

Just as Kailasha is the abode of Shiva, Vaikuntha, situated several hundreds of yojanas above Brahmaloka, is the abode of Vishnu. Here, he spends his leisure with Lakshmi and meets with the devas and sages to discuss their problems. Vaikuntha should not be confused with the Garbhodaka Ocean, although both are depicted as being formed from the coils of Aadishesha. While the former is where Vishnu exists in the worldly form, he exists as Mahavishnu in the latter, in a permanent state of yoganidra.

4

Vritra

A sage once performed a sacrifice to create a demon who would kill Lord Indra, but there was a small problem. When it was time for the final incantations, when the sage should have said, 'May this son of mine be the slayer of Indra', he stressed the wrong syllables in the mantra, changing its meaning to 'May Indra be the slayer of this son of mine.' Such is the uniqueness of the Sanskrit language, where a single word can have several meanings and the only way to differentiate between them is by paying attention to how they are pronounced! So, who was this terrible demon who was born to kill Indra and how was he killed? Read on to find out.

Indra was distraught. He had unwittingly insulted Devaguru Brihaspati, who stormed out of Devaloka in a rage and vanished without a sign. Left in a quandary, without their guru to instruct and advise them, the devas faced one humiliating loss after another in their battles against the asuras. Desperate, Indra approached Brahma for advice.

'Trisira, the son of Tvasta, is a great yogi. He will make an ideal guru for you,' said Brahma. 'But remember, Indra, a guru is equal in stature to the gods themselves and it will be a shame if you lose Trisira to your arrogance, the way you lost Brihaspati. Control yourself and learn to respect those around you!' he reprimanded before sending Indra away.

Leaving Brahma's abode, Indra went looking for Trisira. After a long search, he found the three-headed sage performing the Panchagni Sadhana, a severe penance that involved hanging upside down a tree branch and meditating without consuming food or water. Impressed with Trisira's devotion and yogic powers, Indra requested him to become the guru of the devas.

Trisira accepted and moved to Devaloka, where he regularly performed yagnas to increase the strength of the devas. Soon, the devas were winning their battles against the asuras once again. Indra was pleased.

However, Trisira was not a regular sage. Although his father was a sage and well-wisher of the devas, his mother Rachana was the daughter of Diti, the mother of daityas. This made him half asura. Although it did not bother Indra at first, he was worried by some of Trisira's actions. During the yagnas, the new Devaguru would recite prayers with one head even as he consumed Soma, the divine nectar, with the other and drank wine with the third. And though his rituals were helping the devas defeat the asuras, Trisira never seemed pleased. Indra was not wrong to worry.

'Why should only the devas win all the battles? Why should the asuras suffer?' Trisira had started to ask himself. 'After all, the asuras are my relatives too. Shouldn't I be impartial?' And so, he decided to pray equally for the success of the devas and asuras.

Soon, the battles between the rivals started to end with no clear winner. Indra was not happy. 'What is the secret behind the sudden surge in the asuras' strength?' he wondered.

During the next yagna that Trisira conducted, Indra sat next to him and noticed that while the Devaguru offered oblations in the name of the devas loudly, he also secretly offered prayers for the benefit of the asuras. Enraged at this act of treachery, Indra drew his sword and cut off Trisira's heads.

The entire Devaloka trembled at this act. Killing a sage, that too during a yagna, was considered the gravest of sins; and Indra had killed no ordinary sage but the Guru of the Devas himself!

When Tvasta came to know about the slaying of his son, he flew into a rage. Plucking a strand of hair from his head, he dropped it in the sacrificial fire and vowed to avenge the death of Trisira. He then set about preparing for a great yagna that would give him a son who would slay Indra. During the yagna, a terrible asura child rose from the sacrificial fire and immediately grew into an immense being as large as a mountain. With blazing eyes and tongue, he had a countenance that made the three worlds tremble with fear. But Tvasta did not stop. As he continued with his sacred chants, the demon became more and more powerful until he finally stepped out of the flames with a magical trident in his hand and filled the air with his hot breath. Bowing before Tvasta, he said, 'Command me, O father! What is it that you wish me to do?'

Tvasta was pleased with his creation. 'Son, I hereby name you Vritra. Know now that the only purpose of your life is to seek and kill Indra. Go and avenge your slain brother!'

Vritra bowed before his father with folded hands and said, 'Father, I shall do as you command, but please permit me to first meditate on the name of Devi, the Supreme Goddess. I might be vast as a mountain and stronger than the strongest being, but I am still not immortal. I wish to correct this by asking her for a boon.'

Thus, with his father's blessings, Vritra spent a hundred years doing extreme penance to please Devi. When Devi finally appeared before him and offered to grant a boon, he said, 'Please let it be that I cannot be killed with any weapon that has been made until today. Furthermore, the weapon that would ultimately kill me should be neither wet nor dry and should be made from neither wood nor stone nor metal.'

Armed with the boon, Vritra set out to seek Indra. Knowing that his rival was the controller of the rains, Vritra's first act was to gather all the water of the universe into himself, causing the three worlds to face severe drought. He then proceeded to Devaloka.

Seeing the mighty Vritra flying towards their domain, the devas were agitated. They shot arrows by the thousands towards him; but to Vritra, the arrows were nothing more than tiny thorns. He opened his humungous mouth and swallowed them in one gulp.

'Where is Indra?' Vritra roared upon reaching Devaloka, even as the devas ran helter-skelter in a bid to save their lives. 'Where is he hiding, the coward who slayed my brother? Bring him to me and I shall spare you all!'

Indra realized that the time had come to pay the price for killing Trisira. The drought brought about by the demon had already weakened his people; it wasn't right to let them bear the consequences of his mistake. However, how was he to fight with someone as powerful as Vritra? With no guru to advise him, he approached Vishnu.

'You are right, Indra, Vritra is your demon to fight and conquer. However, he has a unique boon from Devi herself because of which no weapon you wield can slay him. You must go to Sage Dadhichi, for only a weapon crafted from his bones will help you in your task.'

'But...how can I ask Sage Dadhichi to give up his life so I can use his bones? This is not right!' Indra cried.

'True, it is not right. But Dadhichi will understand. He has been meditating upon my name for hundreds of years now; he knows that his mortal body is no longer of use to him,' Vishnu said.

And so, Indra went to Dadhichi's ashram to ask him for his bones. As Vishnu had predicted, the sage had no qualms about giving up his life for the benefit of the devas. He sat in meditation and within no time, his soul merged with that of Vishnu's, leaving behind his body. Indra took the sage's bones to Vishwakarma, the architect of the devas, who crafted a deadly mace—Vajra, out of them.

As soon as Indra lifted the Vajra, a strange energy surged through his body, increasing his confidence and raising his spirits manifold. Mounting his elephant, Airavata, he went forth to confront Vritra.

When Vritra saw the killer of his brother, he was filled with rage. 'Finally, I get to fight the slayer of my brother!' he roared, sending a tremor through Devaloka. He then threw his flaming magical trident towards Indra. However, Indra destroyed it with his Vajra and rushing towards his rival, cut off both his arms.

As Vritra stood armless on the battlefield, the devas rejoiced the defeat of the fearsome demon. Angered by the premature celebration, Vritra drew a deep breath. Then, opening his expansive mouth, he swallowed Indra, who had come charging towards him on Airavata.

The entire Devaloka fell into an uneasy silence. The demon had devoured Indra! What would happen now?

Though caught by surprise at being sucked into Vritra, Indra remained calm. He struck the demon's stomach with the Vajra and caused it to tear open. When Indra came out of Vritra's abdomen, the devas were astounded, but they were still wary. The demon was alive despite his stomach having been torn open. 'Nothing seems to bring an end to Vritra! How can he be killed?' was the question on everyone's mind.

Realizing that Vritra could not be slayed so easily, Indra

prayed to Devi, who appeared before him and said, 'O Indra, Vritra cannot be killed with a weapon that is either wet or dry.'

'Then I shall kill him with the foam from the sea!' Indra replied.

He then dipped the Vajra in sea foam and struck Vritra on his head. The blow sent the massive frame of the demon crumbling to the ground and soon, Vritra was dead. With his death, all the water that he had consumed flowed back into the universe, ending the horrible drought.

Note

It is said that although the devas rejoiced at the death of Vritra, Indra was consumed by the guilt of having killed the demon who had emerged from a holy sacrifice. Moreover, he had also sinned by killing Trisira, his own guru. Tormented by the thought for years together, he finally decided to leave Devaloka and retire to Manasa Lake. There, hiding in the stalk of a lotus, he did penance for thousands of years to repent his grave misdeeds.

Upon hearing about her husband's death, Dadhichi's pregnant wife, Suvarcha, cursed the devas that they would forever remain childless. Then, after giving birth to a son Pippalada, she too gave up her life. Pippalada was brought up by the trees in the forest, while Chandra, the moon, nurtured him with nectar. When he was old enough, he prayed to Shiva for a hundred years and asked for the destruction of the devas, who had been the cause of his parents' death. As per Shiva's advice, he meditated for years together until he could perceive the former's third eye in his own mind's eye. Immediately, a ferocious demon emerged from nowhere.

'You have been nurtured by Chandra and so, you too are a deva; and all devas are my enemies!' the demon proclaimed and charged towards Pippalada.

Realizing his mistake, Pippalada ran to Shiva, who destroyed the demon. Pippalada went on to become a great sage in his own right and wrote the *Prashna Upanishad*.

5

Taraka

The rivalry between the devas and asuras was like that between siblings. Sometimes, they fought because there was a real reason to do so and something important was at stake but mostly, it was simply to seek revenge for a past act by the rival. Taraka was one such asura, whose sole purpose was to avenge his mother and to achieve this end, he prayed to Brahma and asked for a boon, setting a seemingly impossible condition for his death. What was it that happened to Taraka's mother and what impossible condition did he set? Let's find out.

❖

Once, Devi Diti, the mother of all daityas, was upset. Indra and the other devas had killed several asuras in the past and she was filled with a desire to avenge the death of her sons. Seeing her misery, Sage Kashyapa blessed her to have a son who would be indestructible. Thus was born Vajranga.

When Vajranga grew up, he defeated Indra, made him a prisoner and brought him to his mother. Diti sneered at Indra and set him free, remarking that she would rather he lived in the shame of subjugation than die. Despite being a daitya, Vajranga was mellow and had no wish to follow the path of his predecessors. Having fulfilled his duty towards his mother, he retired to the forest with his wife Varangi to live a simple life and perform tapas.

In the meantime, Indra seethed with anger in Devaloka. Unable to forget the humiliation he suffered, he chose a time when Vajranga was away in the forest performing penance to extract revenge. Taking the form of first a monkey, and then a sheep, he uprooted every tree and ate all the grass around Vajranga's hut. Indra then transformed himself into a snake, intending to bite Varangi, who was waiting for her husband's return.

Upon his return, Vajranga was enraged at the destruction and the plight of his wife, who, although she had thwarted Indira's attack, was in despair. He prayed to Brahma and asked for a son who would defeat Indra and torment the devas for a long time. Soon after, the couple was blessed with a son, Taraka, who stayed in Varangi's womb for a thousand years. When he finally emerged, he brought along with him great earthquakes and tempests across the universe. The parents were filled with great joy.

Taraka grew up to be a fearsome demon whose only aim was to defeat the devas and avenge Indra's insult of his mother. So, he left home for the mountains to perform extreme penance. For a hundred years, Taraka prayed to Brahma without eating a morsel of food. For the next hundred years, he consumed only dried leaves as he prayed. Yet, it was only after another hundred years of consuming nothing but water as he meditated that Brahma appeared before him.

'Stop, Taraka!' said Brahma. 'You have shown me great devotion. What boon can I grant you?'

'I want to fight the devas and avenge my mother,' replied Taraka. 'Please grant me the boon that I may be immortal and invincible.'

'All beings have to die, Taraka,' said Brahma. 'So, you can set as difficult a condition as you want for your death, but immortality is not a boon I can grant.'

'Then, O Lord, please grant me that I can only be killed by a seven-year-old son born to Shiva,' requested Taraka.

'So be it,' said Brahma, smiling a knowing smile.

Taraka was pleased. Shiva's wife Sati had just died without bearing him a child; devastated, Shiva was unlikely to marry anytime soon.

Armed with the knowledge that he was invincible and almost immortal, Taraka soon raised a large army and, with the help of his brothers Surapadman and Simhamukha, and other asura friends such as Mahisha, Kujambha, Kaalanemi, Jambhaka, Megha, Manthana and Shumbha, he declared war against the devas.

Feeling threatened by the infallible enemy, Indra sent Vayu as an emissary to broker peace, but Taraka wasn't interested. His army attacked the devas repeatedly until the latter were vanquished. After taking over Devaloka and establishing his reign, Taraka married and had three fearless sons: Tarakaksha, Kamalakaksha and Vidyunmali.

As the asuras ravaged Devaloka for years, Indra was distraught. Aware of the boon granted to Taraka, he ran to Sage Narada for advice. Only Narada's shrewd mind was capable of finding a way to get Shiva married, so he could have a son.

'Don't worry, Indra, I have a solution to your problem,' Narada replied in his singsong voice. 'Go forth to Bhuloka and meet King Himavan and his queen Meena. Sati has been reborn as their daughter Parvati and is already in love with Shiva; she will marry no one else. Take her to Shiva and your work will be done.'

Elated, Indra set about his task immediately. However, Shiva wasn't yet ready to marry. He rejected Parvati, who, deeply disappointed, retreated to the highest caves of the Himalayas to perform tapas. No amount of pleading by the devas could make her change her mind. It was then that the Sapta Rishis (seven great sages) approached Shiva.

'O great Lord, we know that you are still mourning the loss of Sati and it is not in our place to ask you to marry again. But the world needs to be saved from the terrors of Taraka and the only one who can kill him is a son born to you. So, we beg you to marry Parvati, who is so in love with you. She has vowed to remain a tapasvi (ascetic) all her life if she cannot be with you.'

After much persuasion, Shiva finally consented to the wedding. Soon after, a six-headed son—Shanmuka (also known as Kartikeya)—was born to him and Parvati. The gods and devas showered the boy with gifts of toys, accessories and weapons and made him the leader of the devas' army on his seventh birthday.

'What do you want from me?' Shanmukha asked the huge gathering in front of him.

'Only that you slay Taraka and relieve us from our misery,' the devas cried in unison.

'So be it,' said Shanmukha and declared war on the asuras.

When Taraka saw Shanmuka astride his peacock at the battlefield, he laughed. The years of living in the luxuries of Devaloka had made him forget the condition he had laid down to get the boon of invincibility from Brahma.

'What is a boy like you doing here?' he sneered in arrogance. 'Are the cowardly devas going to hide behind a child now? Even the Brahmastra levelled at me by the human king Muchkunda could do me no harm! So, go away and play with a toy instead.'

'This is a battlefield, Taraka, not a place for idle talk,' Shanmukha repiled. 'I may be a child, but remember, war is won by the power of the mind, not physical strength. Even a tiny snake can slay a giant by injecting him with poison. So worry not about my age and instead, show me you are worth the weapons you wield.'

Taraka was incensed at being mocked by a child. He flung

his club at Shanmukha, only to find it being repelled with his rival's Chakra. The asura then hurled an axe at Shanmukha, who effortlessly caught it with his hands. In retaliation, he struck Taraka with a mace that made an ear-shattering sound as it whooshed towards the asura. In the fierce battle that followed, Taraka hurled all sorts of weapons at Shanmukha, but the boy repelled all of these and started to massacre the asura army with his own weapons. Soon, both Surapadman and Simhamukha were slayed and even powerful asuras like Kaalanemi fled the battlefield in dismay. No one had thought that a child would be responsible for the defeat of the most powerful asura army.

Seeing his soldiers desert him, Taraka made a last attempt by hitting Shanmukha's peacock. This infuriated Shanmukha, who threw his spear at Taraka with a force and speed that blinded the asura's vision. Taraka ran all over the battlefield, trying to avoid the spear, but the weapon finally caught up with him and pierced him in the chest.

As Taraka's mountain-like body fell to the ground, his request to Brahma to be slayed by the seven-year-old son of Shiva flashed in front of his eyes and no sooner had he realized his folly, than the mighty asura was dead.

Note

According to the *Skanda Purana*, even as the devas rejoiced, Shanmukha was saddened after killing Taraka, who was a devotee of his father, Shiva. As he sought a means to atone his sin, Vishnu asked him to pray to Shiva himself for forgiveness. Shanmukha then installed a Shivalinga and, sprinkling holy water on it, prayed for the deliverance of Taraka's soul.

6

Mahisha

What happens when a powerful asura king falls in love with a she-buffalo and marries her? Sounds weird, doesn't it? Yet, that is how things played out and set the stage for the birth of one of the most notorious demons in Hindu mythology. Such was his strength, powers of illusion and ability to shape-shift that he brought even Vishnu to his heels in battle. Who was this demon and how was he finally defeated? Read on to know more.

✣

ambha and Karambha were the sons of Sage Kashyapa and Devi Danu. Growing up, the brothers developed a strong dislike for the devas and resolved to, one day, establish the rule of danavas in the three worlds. Realizing that they would require special powers to achieve their goal, they decided to perform penance to please the devas themselves. So, Rambha stood inside a burning fire and prayed to Agni, while Karambha submerged himself in water and prayed to Varuna.

The asura brothers continued with their penance for several years, hoping for the respective devas to appear before them and grant them their boons.

However, Indra sensed there was something amiss.

'Why would the danava brothers worship us devas?' he thought. 'Agni and Varuna are gullible and easy to please. If they grant whatever boon Rambha and Karambha seek, it would lead to the annihilation of us all. There must be a way to stop them!'

After much deliberation, Indra decided to act on his own. Taking the form of a crocodile, he entered the waters where Karambha stood in meditation and killed him. He then proceeded to where Rambha was meditating. However, when he entered the fire, Agni intervened and saved Rambha's life. Then, pleased with Rambha's devotion, Agni offered him a boon.

'O Agni, grant me the boon that I may not be killed by any living being. Only a dead man can be the cause of my death,' Rambha said.

Hearing Rambha's wish, Agni realized his folly; but it was

too late to retract and so, he pronounced a reluctant, 'So be it!'

Upon returning to his kingdom, Rambha was furious to know that Karambha had been killed by Indra. Secure with the knowledge that he was virtually immortal, he started torturing the devas and killing the sages and their followers on Bhuloka. Once, as he returned to his kingdom after a fiery battle, he saw a water buffalo resting in the forest. Unknown to him, the buffalo was a beautiful demon princess who had been cursed to live the life of a mahishi (Sanskrit for 'she-buffalo'). Despite inhabiting the body of an animal, her exceptional beauty radiated in all directions and Rambha, sensing something special about her, fell in love with her. Changing himself into a water buffalo, he abandoned his kingdom to live with her. Rambha and his wife spent several years together and gave birth to a child, Mahisha, who had the unique power to change his form at will.

Soon after Mahisha's birth, Rambha returned to his kingdom and, seeing that the devas had trounced the asuras during his absence, decided to regain his clan's lost glory. Gathering a massive army, he attacked Devaloka. In the battle that followed, when Indra sent his Vajra hurling towards him, Rambha roared with laughter.

'Don't you know that no living being can bring any harm my way? Why waste your effort in trying to kill me?' he asked Indra.

However, in his arrogance, Rambha had forgotten that the Vajra had been crafted from the bones of the dead Sage Dadhichi. As soon as the weapon hit Rambha, he was killed.

Back in Patalaloka, Mahisha grew up to be a strong and

intelligent asura, but he nursed a hatred for the devas since they had been the cause of his father's death. When he was old enough, he took command over the asuras as their king and decided to confront the devas in battle. Before that though, he retreated to the solitude of the mountains to pray to Brahma. After hundreds of years of severe penance, Brahma appeared before Mahisha.

'Grant me that I may be invincible and that death may not come to me because of any animal, man or deva. Grant me also that neither you nor Vishnu nor Shiva can slay me,' Mahisha asked of Brahma.

'So be it,' Brahma said. 'But let it be known Mahisha that no one can escape death, so death will come to you in the form of a woman.'

'Ha ha ha!' Mahisha's laughter thundered across the universe. 'Women are weak and fragile. What harm can they bring to me? I am not one to be scared of them!' he said, even as Brahma smiled a silent smile and disappeared.

Armed with his boon, Mahisha gathered an enormous army and conquered the entire Bhuloka. He then set out to fight the devas. When Indra saw the asuras approaching, he was worried. Mahisha wanted to avenge the death of his father and he would stop at nothing to accomplish his goal. Fearing the worst, he, along with the other devas, asked Vishnu and Shiva to join in the battle against Mahisha. Then, secure with the knowledge that the gods would fight for them if the need arose, the devas entered the battlefield.

Thus, on one side of the battlefield stood Indra, Yama, Surya, Vayu, Varuna, Agni and all the other devas while on the other side stood ruthless asuras such as Shikshura, Tamra, Asiloma, Utharaka, Bidala, Bashkala, Trinetra, Kalabandhaka, Chanda, Munda, Raktabeeja and many more under the leadership of Mahisha. Soon, a ferocious battle ensued, with the asuras matching the devas strength for strength and weapon for weapon. Then, seeing that the battle was headed nowhere, Mahisha decided to use his 'Shaambri Shakti' or the power of illusion. Closing his eyes, he created thousands of Mahishas, who charged into the battlefield with a ferociousness that struck fear amongst the devas.

The terrified devas prayed to Shiva and Vishnu to come to their aid and, encouraged by their presence, started to fight with the asura army once again. In the battle that followed, Vishnu hit Mahisha on the head with Kaumodaki, his mace, causing him to fall to the ground in a faint. However, the asura king soon regained consciousness and assumed the form of a giant buffalo. He then charged towards Vishnu with all his strength and knocked him down. Such was the force of the blow that Vishnu had to retire to his abode in Vaikuntha to recuperate.

The devas were stunned. Here was an asura who had brought Vishnu to his heels! And now, having assumed the form of a buffalo, he was wreaking havoc amongst the army of devas. Unable to withstand his fearsome onslaught, the devas fled from the battlefield and went to Vaikuntha along with Shiva and Brahma.

'O Vishnu, what do we do now? Mahisha's strength seems only to be multiplying every time we confront him. Is there no way to defeat him?' Indra implored.

Seeing the plight of the devas, Brahma spoke up. 'O Indra, remember that I have granted Mahisha the boon that only a woman would be able to kill him. Hence, we must pray to Devi, the Supreme Goddess, to intervene before all is lost!'

When Devi appeared before them, the devas said, 'O Devi, you who is free from the cycle of life and death, whose very being is both an illusion and the truth, we pray to you to deliver us from the atrocities of Mahisha. None other than you can slay him, so have mercy on us; you are our only hope.'

Hearing her praise, Devi smiled and replied, 'Do not fear. Mahisha's boon has made him too arrogant to realize that his end is near. I shall march to Devaloka, where he has established his rule and destroy him.' Then, closing her eyes, she spread out her arms and from within her emerged a fiery bolt of energy that took the form of Durga.

With a chiselled face emanating an extraordinary radiance, eyes as fiery as Agni, and with eighteen arms, Durga sat on her mount, a ferocious lion gifted to her by the mountains. Spellbound at her magnificence, the devas fell at her feet and presented her with all their weapons. Indra gave her his Vajra, Varuna offered her his conch and Pasha, a noose capable of capturing hundreds of demons at one go, Agni gifted his weapon Shatagni, Vayu gave her his divine bow and a quiver that would never run out of arrows and Yama offered his sceptre. Then, Shiva and Vishnu stepped forward to arm Durga with their trident and discus, respectively, while Brahma gave her a vessel filled with holy water.

Satisfied with her creation, Devi said, 'Go forth, Durga,

and bring Mahisha to the end he wished for!'

Upon reaching Devaloka, Durga proclaimed her arrival with a terrifying roar that reverberated across the three worlds. Mahisha immediately sent his soldiers to find out who had dared to disturb his peace. Seeing the three-eyed Durga perched upon her lion at the gates, the soldiers ran back to him and described both her enchanting beauty and her ferociousness.

'We do not know who she is or where she has come from. But this we know—with long black hair, a radiant face, eyebrows arched like bows and lips supple and red as blood, she is far more beautiful than any apsara; with eighteen arms, each holding a different weapon, and three fiery eyes, she is more terrifying than any warrior we have seen!' they said.

'More beautiful than an apsara! Who could she be?' Mahisha thought, fascinated by the description delivered to him. Summoning his minister, he said, 'Go, bring her to me immediately. If she is indeed as beautiful as the soldiers have described, I wish to make her my wife!'

However, Durga dismissed his proposal and instead said, 'Tell Mahisha that he has two choices. He could either restore Devaloka to its rightful owners and return to his own abode in Patala, or he could choose to battle with me.'

Mahisha laughed upon hearing Durga's message. 'Battle with a woman indeed!' he said. 'When I have defeated Vishnu himself, what will a frail beauty accomplish by battling me? But I cannot say no to her lest the world considers me a coward. So tell her to prepare for war, for I will meet her in the battlefield at the break of dawn tomorrow!'

The next day, Mahisha sent a massive army to fight Durga. Chakshusa, Tamra, Udagra, Asiloma, Durmukha and Bhashkala—the fearsome generals of his army—lead the Chaturangani Sena comprising a crore of asuras on foot, and crores and crores more on horses, chariots and elephants. Without a flinch, Durga entered the battlefield on her lion and blew her conch. Then, with a single exhaled breath, she created millions of warriors who charged towards the asura army with all their might.

When the war commenced, Bhashkala was the first to be killed by Durga as her trident pierced through him. She then marched towards Durmukha, broke his bow, damaged his chariot with her arrows and finally slashed his head with her sceptre. When Chakshusa and Tamra charged towards her, her lion tore their body to pieces. With the death of each asura commander, Durga's ferociousness increased manifold. Even as her army battled the asura warriors, she chose the strongest of her rivals to fight against. Soon, she had burnt the asuras Asiloma, Maha Hanu, Ugrastha and Ugraveerya with the fiery blaze radiating from her third eye and had slashed Bidala, Durdara and Kala into pieces.

Mahisha was astounded when he heard of the death of some of his most trusted commanders. However, he was now more curious than ever about this woman who had suddenly arrived at his doorstep and caused such destruction. Transforming himself into a handsome man, he went to the battlefield to confront Durga and was smitten the moment he laid eyes on her. 'O beautiful one, I have already been slain by your magnificence! Marry me and live with me forever; we can avoid more bloodshed if you accept my proposal,' he said.

'Mahisha! You have come to me at last!' Durga spoke. 'But mistake not; I am here not to submit to your desires but to take your life, for is that not what you chose? To be killed by a woman? So pick up your arms and face me in battle...or would you rather go back to Patala and hide from me?'

Durga's words stung Mahisha. Furious, he turned himself into a buffalo and circled her, snorting and violently swishing his tail. Even as the thump of his hooves on the battlefield caused sandstorms and earthquakes across the universe, his heavy breathing made the mountains shiver. Mahisha wrapped his tail around one such mountain and uprooting it, hurled it towards Durga, accepting her challenge.

'I have defeated Vishnu himself, why would I fear fighting you?' he roared and charged towards Durga, who tossed the Pasha around his neck and pulled him closer. However, Mahisha escaped the noose by transforming into a lion that pounced in an attempt to gore her lion. When Durga sent a volley of arrows to deter him, he immediately morphed into an elephant and hurled huge boulders towards her.

Even as Durga used the Vajra to shatter the rocks, Mahisha took the form of a giant serpent so he could strangle her. In reply, Durga sent several arrows towards him that turned into snakes and fought with him until he changed form once again. Thus, the fight between the two continued for eight-long days and nights, with Mahisha changing form after form hoping to take Durga by surprise and attack her and Durga deftly repelling every attack.

On the ninth day, Durga grew impatient. Surveying the

battlefield with fiery red eyes, she blew her conch with a force that sent the waves of the oceans surging as high as the skies. The asura army stopped its fight for a moment and stared at Durga as she drank the divine nectar called Soma Rasa from the chalice gifted to her by Kubera and let out a beastly roar. Then, even as Mahisha transformed himself into his original form of a buffalo and charged towards her, Durga tamed him with her noose and beheaded him.

However, Mahisha wasn't ready to give up just yet; he changed back into human form and began to emerge from the torso of the buffalo. Ever alert, Durga's lion pounced upon him and pinned him to the ground. Durga then left her mount and, stomping Mahisha down to the ground, drove her trident through his heart and killed him.

Note

According to the *Skanda Purana*, Durga found a Shivalinga stuck in Mahisha's throat after she severed his head. The discovery made her realize that the asura was, in fact, a staunch devotee of Shiva. Feeling remorseful, she is said to have done penance to repent the killing of Mahisha and seek pardon from Shiva.

7

Mahishi

A sage once cursed his own wife that she would be reborn as a she-buffalo. The wife, in turn, cursed him that he too would take birth as a buffalo and fall in love with her. Strange as it sounds, things transpired exactly as the curses had spelt them out. But why are we talking about buffaloes rather than demons? Well, the only way to find out is to read on.

Mahisha had just been killed by Durga. The devas rejoiced in Devaloka, but there was nothing but grief and despair among the asuras. In her chambers, Mahishi, the she-buffalo demoness, roared in anguish. Mahisha, her cousin, had been very dear to her and his death left her shattered.

'Revenge!' she cried. 'I shall seek revenge for my brother's death. I shall make life miserable for every deva who participated in the killing of Mahisha...so miserable that they'll beg to be killed!'

Before setting out on her task though, she decided to pray to Brahma. For several hundred years, she meditated on Brahma's name until one day, he appeared before her and offered to grant her a boon. Mahishi was cunning. She knew Brahma would never grant her the boon of immortality, so she asked that she meet her death only at the hands of a son born to Shiva and Vishnu.

'Ha ha!' she sniggered when Brahma agreed to her condition. 'How will two male beings ever give birth to a child! Brahma is so gullible...and I am now truly immortal.'

Then, arrogance took over her and she went about destroying everything that came her way. Soon, she had conquered the three worlds and established her rule over Devaloka, displacing Indra from his throne.

Unable to bear the insult, Indra approached Vishnu for help.

'Remember, Indra, Mahishi was Leela, the wife of Sage Dattatreya, in her previous birth. She has been born as a buffalo-headed demoness due to a curse by her own husband.'

'Why would her own husband curse her, my Lord?' Indra asked, curious.

'There was a time when, tired of all things worldly,

Dattatreya wanted to retire to the forests and live the life of a sanyasi but Leela wasn't ready to give up the comforts and pleasures of life.

Enraged, Dattatreya cursed her to be born as a buffalo. Not to be outdone, Leela also cursed him back saying he too would be born as a buffalo and fall in love with her.'

'But what use is this story of buffaloes to me!' Indra cried in frustration.

'Don't you see, Indra? The only way to draw Mahishi out of Devaloka is to arrange for Dattatreya's rebirth!' So saying, Vishnu summoned Brahma, who set about the task.

Soon, a handsome male buffalo, Sundara Mahisha, took form and set off for Devaloka. When Mahishi set eyes on him, she instantly fell in love with him and charmed, she agreed to leave Devaloka and live in the forests on Bhuloka with him. In her absence, the devas managed to fight away the asura army and regain their abode. However, they were not destined to enjoy for long.

Once, Sage Durvasa offered Indra a special garland presented to him by Shiva. Instead of wearing it around his neck, Indra placed the garland on the trunk of Airavata, his elephant, who, inebriated by its fragrance, shook it off and caused it to fall on the ground.

Durvasa was beyond himself with anger. 'O Indra, such is your impudence that the garland I conferred upon you now lies on the ground! For this, I shall curse you. May it be that you and your entire clan lose all your powers and turn into old, ugly and sickly beings. May it be that you lose all that is precious to you. And may it be that just as my garland was cast on the ground, your supremacy over the three worlds shall also be cast down!'

As soon as the sage uttered his curse, the devas were shorn of their strength and lustre and their most precious possessions, including the divine earrings of Aditi, the umbrella of Varuna, the seven-headed horse Uchchaisravas and the Airavata, disappeared into nothingness. Dejected, Indra prayed to Vishnu, who advised that the only way to regain all that the devas had lost would be to perform Samudra Manthan by churning the Ksheera Sagara.

This being a difficult task, the devas lured the asuras to join hands with them, promising to share the Amrut, the nectar of immortality, that would emerge from the Ocean. After thousands of years of churning, the Ocean finally started to spit out the lost treasures of the devas that had remained hidden in its underbelly. Along with these came several other wondrous gifts such as fourteen precious gems, the apsaras, Lakshmi, the Goddess of Wealth, Chandra, the handsome Moon God, Varuni, the Goddess of Intoxication, Kalpavriksha, the wish-fulfilling tree, and Kamadhenu, the cow of plenty. Dividing these amongst themselves, the devas and asuras continued with the churning until finally, Dhanvantri emerged from the Ocean carrying a pot of Amrut. However, just as the devas were about to reach for it, the asuras snatched it away. Seeing the devas in distress, and knowing well the havoc the asuras would unleash once they gained immortality, Vishnu decided to intervene. He took the form of a dazzling beauty, Mohini, and appeared in front of the asuras, who immediately started to fight among themselves so each could take her as his wife.

To settle the matter, Mohini asked the asuras to close their eyes, saying she would marry the one who was the last to open them. Then, as the naïve asuras did as they were told, Mohini grabbed the pot of nectar and fled to Devaloka.

When Shiva heard about Vishnu's prank, he expressed his wish to see Mohini. 'Can you really be so beautiful as to cause a fight between the asuras?' he asked in all innocence.

At first, Vishnu was reluctant to show Shiva his feminine form, but when he finally relented and transformed into Mohini, Shiva could not help falling in love with her. From their union was born a son, Ayyappa, also known as Hari-Hara Putra.

When Vishnu returned to his original form, he was astounded. 'What will we do with this child now?' he wondered.

'Don't worry, O Vishnu,' said Brahma, appearing before him. 'This child has been born for a purpose...to slay Mahishi. So, send him to Bhuloka, where the childless King Rajashekhara has been praying for years for an heir to his throne. When the time is right, this very child will fulfil the purpose of his birth.'

And so, Ayyappa was sent to Bhuloka. Two years later, the queen gave birth to her own child and both children were raised with the same love and care. However, when Ayyappa turned twelve, the king decided to make him the crown prince rather than his own son. This irked the queen and she suddenly started hating Ayyappa. She wanted to do away with him so that her son would be the only one to lay claim to the throne. Feigning an illness that could be cured only by drinking a tigress's milk, she sent Ayyappa into the forest to look for the same. In her heart, she hoped he would be killed by the tigress.

It was in this same forest that Mahishi lived with Sundara Mahisha. Having come to know about the asuras being driven out of Devaloka, she had been plotting vengeance for long. Now, finding an opportune moment, she rushed to Devaloka, producing thousands of dreaded creatures from the follicles of her hair to wreak havoc all around them.

Ayyappa was wandering through the forest in search of a tigress when the devas descended in front of him and reminded him of the purpose of his birth. Soon, he accompanied the devas to their abode and fought with Mahishi in a ferocious battle before catching her by her horns and hurling her down to Bhuloka, to her death.

Note

The story goes that Dattatreya was furious when his wife Leela wanted to live in the comforts of their ashram when he had decided to give it all up and retire to the forests.

'You want to live like a Mahishi? Fine, I curse you to become a Mahishi!' he is said to have thundered.

You might wonder what this curse meant. Well, in Sanskrit, the word 'Mahishi' has two meanings: queen and she-buffalo. So, while Leela had wanted to live like a queen, she ended up living the life of a she-buffalo! Isn't it interesting how language can be manipulated?

Also, you might be curious as to what happened to Ayyappa after the killing of Mahishi. Well, he is said to have returned to the palace riding on a tiger flanked by many tigresses, who were in fact, Indra and the other devas in disguise. The scene caused a furore in the kingdom. Here was a boy who had been asked to get a tigress's milk, but he'd returned with a group of tigers instead! Even as the entire kingdom bowed to him, the queen realized her mistake and asked him for forgiveness.

8

Simhika

The emotions of a mother are above the trivialities of 'who' she is—animal, human or demoness. While she is an epitome of selfless love for her children, she is also a power to reckon with when it comes to protecting them. One such mother was the demoness Simhika and this is her story.

Simhika was furious. Vishnu had severed the head of Svarabhanu, the eldest of her hundred and one children.

'So what if he wanted to drink the Amrut that emerged

during the Samudra Manthan? After all, didn't he, along with the other asuras, help churn the ocean? Would the sons of Aditi have been able to complete this enormous task without the help of the asuras...and my son?' she thought to herself. She was still pacing the floor of her chamber, seething with anger, when a monstrous head and a headless body flew in.

'Who are you?' she asked, alarmed at the strange sight.

'Mother, we are your son Svarabhanu!' the head and torso chorused.

'What? How can it be? Vishnu has slain my son!' cried Simhika.

'No, Mother, it is true that he severed my head, but I did not die for I had already consumed a drop of the Amrut. However, as you can see, I am no longer just one being but two! I, the head of Svarabhanu, am henceforth to be known as Rahu.'

'And I am to be known as Ketu,' the headless torso interjected.

Simhika was aghast. 'How dare Vishnu do this to my son! I shall seek vengeance,' she screamed.

Sure, her brother Prahalad was a great devotee of Vishnu, but that did not matter. How could it, when Vishnu was partial towards Aditi's sons and did not care for the asuras? Her father, the great asura king Hiranyakashipu, was right; there was only one Lord to be worshipped and that was him!

'No, Mother,' Rahu's voice interrupted her thoughts. 'The discus that cut your son's throat was Vishnu's to be sure, but this was not entirely his doing. In fact, we would blame only

Surya and Chandra for our wretched state. If they hadn't told Vishnu, he would not have come to know that your son, who looked no less resplendent than the other devas, was in fact an asura. It is them who need to be punished!' he continued, narrating the incident where Vishnu, in the form of Mohini, had been ready to pour the Amrut into Svarabhanu's chalice, when Surya and Chandra told on him.

'Then I shall make sure they pay the price for their audacious deed!' Simhika roared.

She stormed out of her chambers and, leaving the palace behind, headed to the mountains to undertake an extreme penance. For several years, she meditated on the name of Brahma without caring for food or water until he appeared before her.

'Please grant me the boon that I can control anyone by touching their shadow,' she asked of Brahma, who, though puzzled with the strange request, granted it to her.

Simhika then rushed to Surya's abode and took control of Chaaya, the shadow of his wife Sanghya, rendering both of them paralysed, with no control over their own movements. Chaaya tried to shout for help, but Simhika pressed her throat until no voice emerged from it. 'Let Surya feel the same pain that I felt upon seeing the loathsome treatment meted out to my son!' she said, her voice dripping with revulsion.

As days passed, her unique boon made Simhika more and more arrogant. 'Wherever there is either Surya or Chandra, there will be shadows and wherever there are shadows, there will be me to take control of them!' she hollered. Having imprisoned Chaaya, she now sought out more and more beings from Devaloka and soon, she had in her control Anjana, the mother of Hanuman.

Furious, Hanuman asked her to release his mother or meet a dire fate. Simhika let out a thunderous laugh and declined to do so. Instead, seizing an opportune moment, she captured Hanuman's shadow too and brought him under her control.

In the meantime, Surya, who had been perplexed by the piteous state of his wife, realized that it was the doing of Simhika. He immediately set out to confront her.

'Son, I hear that Surya is on his way to fight me. Go right away and stop his approach; engulf him in your enormous mouth if you must!' Simhika commanded Rahu.

'Yes, Mother,' said Rahu and did her bidding. Soon, he had swallowed Surya and plunged the universe into darkness.

With the disappearance of Surya's radiance, shadows across the world too melted away. Finding his mother and himself free from Simhika's control, Hanuman soon overpowered her and made her his prisoner. However, realizing that the reason for Simhika's actions was her love for her son, he offered to set her free if Rahu agreed to release Surya. Seeing his mother in a quandary, Rahu immediately spat out Surya, filling the world with light once again.

While the devas rejoiced at getting back Surya, Hanuman was worried. 'I have promised to set Simhika free, but she still has the power to control us with our shadows. How can I ensure that she doesn't cause trouble over and over again?' he wondered. Then, realizing that her boon made her a nuisance for everyone, he pleaded with Shukracharya, the guru of asuras, to banish Simhika from Patala, while Indra expelled her from Devaloka. With nowhere else to go, Simhika plunged into the depths of the ocean on Bhuloka and made it her abode.

Before she left though, Hanuman sounded her a warning. 'You have caused great grief to all of us, Simhika, but I shall still let you go. Remember though that if you ever cross my path in future, I shall not be so generous; I shall kill you without a second thought!'

Several thousands of years passed by, with Simhika living under the vast ocean, unable to control any being anymore, except the birds flying overhead that cast their shadow on the surface of the water. To satisfy her hunger, she pulled the shadows of the hapless birds and drew them towards her before swallowing them. But these weren't enough to satiate her and with every passing year, her hunger grew manifold.

Then one day, as she scanned the sky from her domain under the waters, Simhika spotted something flying above her. No, it wasn't a bird! 'What can it be?' she wondered, hoping that whatever it was would be large enough to satisfy her hunger.

Unknown to Simhika, the being was none other than Hanuman, who was crossing the Great Ocean to get to Ravana's Lanka. So engrossed was he in chanting the name of Rama that he failed to notice Simhika and was soon under her control as she grabbed his shadow. Finding himself paralysed all of a sudden, Hanuman cast a glance downwards and saw Simhika pulling at him from the ocean floor.

Hanuman smiled. Using his spiritual powers, he started to grow larger and larger in size until he measured a hundred yojanas from head to toe. At first, Simhika was startled; but her hunger blinded her to everything else. All she could think of was that this enormous being would finally satisfy her hunger. So, she opened her mouth wider and wider until it spanned a little more than a hundred yojanas. Just as she was about to swallow Hanuman, though, he shrank his form so that he was now only the size of an ant and jumped into Simhika's open mouth.

Simhika was astounded. Who was this being and how was he able to change his form so quickly? And what would she do about her hunger, now that she had swallowed a being the size of just an ant?

Even as she seethed and fumed at this strange turn of events, Hanuman slashed all her vital organs with his nails and flew out of her open mouth. Screaming and wailing in great pain, Simhika let out a deafening bellow that sent tremors through the three worlds and soon fell dead.

Note

It is said that Rahu and Ketu also prayed to Brahma in the hope of getting out of their plight. When Brahma appeared before them, he split a gigantic snake and joined its body to Rahu and its head to Ketu so that they were complete beings once again. He then granted them the boon that they would each be acknowledged as one of the nine planets or navagrahas, with humans offering them oblations during rituals just as they did to the other devas.

Further, it is said that the solar and lunar eclipse are, in fact, the act of Rahu swallowing Surya and Chandra, respectively, albeit for a short time, thus extracting revenge for their role in Svarabhanu's beheading.

This story is based on one of the many accounts I came across about Simhika. While in all other stories, Simhika from the Vedas (as Swarbhanu's mother) and Simhika from the Ramayana are two separate demonesses, I have chosen to narrate this particular one here because it was fascinating to find a plausible connection between the two with events that were set thousands of years apart!

9

Jalandhara

We all get angry and when in the clutches of that all-consuming anger, we say or do things that we later regret. Have you ever wondered what happens when the gods get angry beyond control? Let's find out.

O nce, when Indra and Sage Brihaspati were on their way to meet Shiva in Kailasa, they came across a hermit blocking their path. At first, Indra enquired as to who the hermit was and what he was doing there, high up in the mountains; but when the hermit remained silent, Indra brusquely asked him to move out of their way. The hermit did not budge; instead, his already radiant face lit up with a soft smile. Arrogance got the better of Indra and thinking the hermit to be impudent, he threatened him with his thunderbolt. No sooner had he done this than his hand became paralysed.

Brihaspati immediately realized that the hermit was none other than Shiva, who had disguised himself to test their devotion. However, the deed was done now; Indra's arrogance had angered Shiva. Brihaspati knew he had to act quickly, lest Shiva threw open his third eye and caused destruction around him, perhaps even kill Indra. He fell at Shiva's feet and started to sing his praises, hoping to calm him down. Extolling his powers as the destroyer of the demon Andhaka, glorifying his status as one of the Trinities, exalting his virtues as the omnipresent who is both the creator and annihilator of time, Brihaspati prayed to Shiva and asked him to pardon Indra.

Shiva was pleased with Brihaspati's words and realized he was being too harsh on Indra, but it was impossible for him to curb the anger that had risen like fire and was ready to burn everything around to ashes. To avoid killing Indra, he sent the fire from his third eye towards the place where Ganga merged with the waters of the ocean. The fire immediately took the form of a baby boy that cried so loudly that the earth and the heavens trembled with fear. Soon, Brahma descended to Bhuloka to find the cause of the turmoil.

Upon seeing Brahma, Varuna, the Ocean God, placed the child on the Creator's lap and asked, 'Who is this boy and where has he come from?'

Even as Brahma contemplated upon an answer, the child, who felt extraordinarily heavy on his lap, tugged at his beard with great force. Brahma cried out in pain and tears started rolling down his eyes. 'Who indeed could this child be?' he wondered.

Closing his eyes, he thought for a while and said, 'O Varuna, I do not know where this child has come from; but I do know this—he will grow up to become the most powerful asura there ever was and will be indestructible, except at the hands of Shiva. Take him and raise him as your own son.' Then, before returning to his abode, he added, 'Since the boy has brought jala (water) to my eyes by his sheer strength, let him be known to the world as Jalandhara, the one who holds water.'

Pleased with Brahma's prophecy, Varuna bowed down to him. He carried the child to his home and brought him up with love and care.

Jalandhara grew to be a handsome man with strength beyond compare. When the time was right, he was crowned the king of all asura kings by their guru Shukracharya and was accepted by his people as a noble and just ruler. Later, he married Vrinda, the daughter of the asura king Kaalanemi and a great devotee of Vishnu. Vrinda loved her husband with all her heart and the enormous yogic powers she gained by her devotion to Vishnu helped Jalandhara become more and more powerful.

Once, noticing Rahu in his court with only a head and no torso, Jalandhara asked Shukracharya about it. The Asura Guru recounted how Vishnu had cut off Svarabhanu's head for daring to taste the Amrut that he had deceitfully procured for the devas after the Samudra Manthan.

The mention of Samudra Manthan caused Jalandhara to flare up. 'The Ocean is my father. How dare the devas loot him and take away all the precious gems and jewels that came out during the churning? Am I not the rightful owner of those treasures now?' With eyes reddened with anger, he summoned his messenger Ghasmara.

'Go, tell that treacherous Indra to return all that he took from the ocean. And let him know that refusal will lead to his annihilation!' Jalandhara thundered.

However, Ghasmara returned from Indra's court empty-handed. He had been sent away saying the Samudra Manthan was done at the behest of Vishnu and whatever the devas had taken away were rightfully theirs.

'And tell your king that Indra is not afraid of him,' Indra had told Ghasmara. 'We have earlier killed Shankhasura, another son of the ocean, and there is nothing to stop us from killing Jalandhara if the need arises!'

Even as Ghasmara trembled with fright as he recounted his meeting with Indra, Jalandhara flew into a rage. He immediately prepared for battle and upon reaching Devaloka with his army, roared like a lion to announce his arrival. A raging battle ensued between the devas and asuras and soon, the battlefield was strewn with dead bodies from both sides.

As the bodies of dead asuras were brought back to their battle camp, Shukracharya got down to work his magic. Using his knowledge of the Mritasanjivani Mantra, a chant to revive the dead that had been taught to him by Shiva after years of performing treacherous penance, he soon began to bring the slain asuras back to life. Jalandhara was overjoyed, but he was also perplexed. It wasn't only the asuras who were being resurrected, the devas too were being revived and sent back to the battle.

'How are the dead devas rising up again, Gurudev?' he asked Shukacharya. 'Isn't the knowledge of Mritasanjivani a secret, known only to you?'

Shukracharya nodded. 'Yes, that is true. However, the devas have Brihaspati on their side and he has been using medicinal herbs from the Drona Mountain to bring the slain devas back to life. Unless the mountain itself is destroyed, there is no way to stop Brihaspati or the devas.'

Enraged, Jalandhara uprooted the Drona Mountain and submerged it in the ocean, thus putting an end to Brihaspati's efforts. Soon, the devas were routed in the battle and Jalandhara established his rule over Devaloka.

Demoralized and desperate, the devas went into hiding and prayed to Vishnu to intervene on their behalf. However, as he set out to challenge the might of the asura king, Lakshmi made Vishnu promise that he would not kill Jalandhara; after all, she too was the daughter of the Ocean and Jalandhara was like a brother to her.

Soon, the three worlds reverberated with sounds from the fierce battle that ensued between Vishnu and Jalandhara. Vishnu used every kind of weapon against his opponent, but Jalandhara reverted with equally powerful weapons and matched Vishnu is every form of fight, be it with weapons or hand-to-hand combat. After years of fighting though,

Vishnu finally came close to beheading Jalandhara, when he remembered the promise he had made to Lakshmi. So, he put down his weapons and said, 'O Jalandhara, I can see that you are blessed, that you are invincible in war. I have slain several terrifying asuras with these same weapons; yet, none of these have had any impact on you. I am delighted with your valour and this has indeed been a great fight, but you must realize that there will be no winner in this battle. So, ask me whatever you want, even that which cannot be given, and I shall grant you that!'

Upon hearing Vishnu's words, Jalandhara bowed down with humility and said, 'O Vishnu, you are the husband of my sister and I have nothing but respect for you! As you must know, my wife Vrinda is a great devotee of yours. So, if you want to grant me a boon, please grant me this: come, live with us in our home.'

Touched by Jalandhara's words, Vishnu forgot all about the battle and accepting his offer, moved into the asura king's palace set in the middle of the Ksheera Sagara along with Lakshmi. The devas were distraught. What could they do, now that Vishnu himself had deserted them? Seeing no other way out, they approached Sage Narada for help.

When he heard about the devas' plight, Narada smiled. He knew that Jalandhara could be killed only by Shiva and no one else, so he would have to hatch a plan to make the two of them meet. After giving it some thought, he reassured the devas and headed to Jalandhara's abode. Upon reaching the asura king's court, Narada showered praises on Jalandhara for having managed to acquire all the riches in the world.

'I have just returned from Kailasa and let me tell you, Jalandhara, that what you have here is equal in splendour to what Shiva has. You have with you Indra's elephant Airavata, Surya's horse Ucchaisravas, Brahma's celestial chariot, the wish-fulfilling Kalpavruksha tree, the richest of Kubera's riches...what else would a great king like you want!' Then, with a mischievous twinkle in his eye, he said, 'But there is one thing Shiva has that you don't. It is a shame, really, but what can be done about it? This is the way of life!'

Jalandhara's curiosity was piqued. 'What is it, Narada? Do tell me!'

'I am talking about Parvati, Shiva's wife. She is the most exquisite beauty there ever was or there ever will be,' so saying, Narada went his way, knowing that he had sown a seed of jealousy in Jalandhara. It would only be a matter of time before the asura king made his way to Kailasa!

Narada was right. His description of Parvati had left Jalandhara smitten and he wanted nothing other than to take her as his wife. But what was he to do with Shiva, her husband? He sent Rahu as his messenger to request Shiva to give up his wife; after all, he was an ascetic, how could he keep Parvati happy on the meagre alms that he received?

Rahu repeated Jalandhara's message word for word when he arrived at Kailasa. Hearing him, Shiva's anger knew no bounds and from his eyebrow sprang a fearsome creature. With a menacing mouth bearing a swaying tongue, with eyes blazing with fiery flames and with hair that stood on their ends on a dry and rough ashen body, the creature rushed towards Rahu with a deafening bellow.

Terrified, Rahu scampered back to Jalandhara and conveyed what had transpired. 'O Jalandhara, if a creature from his brow can be so dreadful, I can't imagine how powerful and frightening Shiva himself would be! It is not advisable to confront him,' he said, still trembling with fear.

However, Jalandhara would have none of it. Agitated over Shiva's refusal, he gathered all the powerful asura kings and their armies and marched towards Kailasa.

Upon reaching there, a fierce battle commenced between the asura army and Shiva's ganas, an army of Shiva's staunch followers that included the bhoothas, naagas, yakshas, pisachas, raksha ganas, guhyakas, vidhyadharas and siddhas, amongst others. As before, Shukracharya revived every asura that was slain in the battle and sent him back to fight, leaving the ganas outnumbered. The asura army seemed very close to victory. In the meantime, Jalandhara easily defeated both Kartikeya and Ganesha and trapped Shiva and his aides inside an illusion created by him. He then disguised himself as Shiva and proceeded to Parvati's abode.

'Parvati, my dear,' he said, upon setting his eyes on the beauty he so coveted, 'I have defeated that wretched Jalandhara!'

But Parvati was not to be conned. She immediately recognized the being in front of her to be an imposter and fled to the Manasa Lake. There, she called upon Vishnu to avenge Jalandhara's impudence.

'Tell me, how could Jalandhara dare to come to me in the guise of my husband? How did he grow to be so powerful?' she asked Vishnu.

'Devi, Jalandhara was always powerful for he is born from a part of Shiva himself. But then, he married Vrinda, who is my greatest devotee. Every time her husband goes to war, Vrinda prays to me and the yogic powers she derives through these prayers ensure that Jalandhara remains invincible.'

'Then you must go to Vrinda and prevent her from praying further!' Parvati commanded.

The next morning, as Vrinda started to pray for her husband's welfare, she saw someone enter her chamber. Turning around, she was shocked to see Jalandhara standing in front of her.

'I am back!' Jalandhara announced. 'I have defeated Shiva and now am truly the lord of all the worlds!'

Happy to have her husband back, Vrinda thanked Vishnu in her prayers, not knowing that he who she was thanking was standing right in front of her, guised in the form of Jalandhara.

Back at Kailasa, the illusion that had trapped Shiva had faded away and a fierce battle was being fought between Shiva and the real Jalandhara. Once again, Jalandhara used his powers to create an illusion of Parvati being tortured by fellow asura kings Shumbha and Nishumbha. The sight demoralized Shiva and he laid down his arms in dejection. Jalandhara seized the opportunity to send three arrows that pierced Shiva's head, chest and belly.

At that very moment, Vrinda stopped saying her prayers and embraced Vishnu, thinking he was her husband. Within a trice, the illusion created by Jalandhara vanished and Shiva, unaffected by the arrows, rose from the battlefield assuming a terrifying, blazing form. He allowed Shumbha and Nishumbha to escape, warning them that they would meet their end at the hands of the very same Parvati they tried to torture. He then turned his attention to Jalandhara.

Creating a sharp chakra by spinning the waters of the ocean with his toe, Shiva sent it flying towards Jalandhara. Without his wife's prayer to protect him, the weapon slashed through Jalandhara's body, beheading and killing him instantaneously.

Realizing that Jalandhara was his own creation, Shiva felt sad at having to annihilate him. So, even as the asura king's flesh and blood were taken away to rot in the hells of Maharaurava, his soul merged with that of Shiva's.

Note

When Vrinda realized that Vishnu had conned her, she was utterly dejected. Not able to bear the truth that the very being to whom she had been devoted all her life had a hand in her husband's death, she cursed Vishnu. 'A day will come, O Vishnu, when your wife will be abducted and taken to someplace far from you. You shall then know what it means to be separated from a loved one and suffer for it!' She then entered the sacred fire and immolated herself. Since she had been extremely devoted and faithful to her husband, Vrinda's soul merged with Parvati's just as her husband's soul had merged with Shiva's.

Remember the ferocious creature that had materialized from Shiva's brow and chased Rahu out of Kailasa? Although he was not an asura, his story is equally interesting. When the creature rushed to eat Rahu, Rahu begged Shiva for mercy and was allowed to return to Jalandhara unharmed. Distraught, the creature complained to Shiva that he was enormously hungry and had nothing to eat since Rahu was allowed to escape. Shiva smiled and in jest, told the being to eat his own hands, legs and abdomen. Ever faithful and devoted to Shiva, the creature did just that—he consumed his own body until nothing but his head remained.

Seeing this, Shiva was extremely pleased. 'You did not think twice before following my order! I bow to you, for you are my greatest devotee. Although you are only a head now, you shall henceforth stand guard to my abode. And you will be known to all as Kirtimukha or the "face of glory".'

You will find it interesting that many Shiva temples, especially in South India, bear the carved motif of Kirtimukha at the entrance to the garbha-griha or inner sanctum.

10

Raktabeeja

After Mahisha's death at the hands of Durga, things went back to being normal in the universe for some time until the danava brothers Shumbha and Nishumbha started spreading their terror. When the time came for them to fight the mighty Devi Kaushiki, they turned to Raktabeeja, a general in Mahisha's army, for help. Raktabeeja himself was an asura with a boon from Brahma that gave him a unique strength. What was this strength that had even the mighty Devi flummoxed for a moment? Read on to find out.

❖

The earth trembled as Raktabeeja roared in anger. His lord and master Mahisha had been slayed by Durga after which she had reincarnated as Kaushiki and taken residence in the Vidhya mountains. All he could think of was extracting revenge. Now, Shumbha and Nishumbha, sons of Devi Danu, had presented him with just the opportunity.

The danava brothers had already trounced the devas and taken over the reins of the three worlds. They wreaked havoc everywhere they went, disturbing the prayers of sages on earth, forcing everyone to worship no one but them and forcefully taking away Indra's Airavata, Yama's buffalo, Varuna's glittering umbrella and Vayu's mace and conch. Then, intoxicated by power and enamoured by her stunning beauty, they demanded Kaushiki to bow down before them and accept either of them as her husband.

'Whoever seeks my hand in marriage will have to defeat me in war,' thundered the Goddess from her lofty abode in the mountains as the danava brothers' messenger Sugriva stood before her with their proposal.

Enraged at Kaushiki's response, Shumbha and Nishumbha sent forth their troop of infallible warriors, headed first by Dhumralochana and then by the daitya brothers Chanda and Munda. But Kaushiki burnt Dhumralochana and his entire army to ashes with her fiery glare and, adopting the form of Kali, beheaded Chanda and Munda. She wore their heads around her neck as ornaments and, adopting the name Chamundi, went on to wipe out whatever remained of the danava army.

That is when Shumbha and Nishumbha turned to

Raktabeeja.

Seeing the terrified danavas run away from the battlefield in an attempt to save their lives, Raktabeeja hollered, 'She, who dared to kill my Lord will now die at my hands!' He then marched to the foothills of the Vindhya mountains with his thirty-akshouhini-strong army.

'Will you dare come down and fight me?' he challenged Kaushiki, 'or would you rather crawl on the ground and beg Shumbha or Nishumbha to marry you?'

'Go back, O ignorant fool and ask your masters to fight me, not send some wretched assistant in their stead,' Kaushiki replied, her laughter reverberating through the three worlds.

Stung by the insult, Raktabeeja started scaling the mountain even as Kaushiki sat back and smiled.

Raktabeeja and his army climbed higher and higher up the mountain, but every time they thought they'd reached the top, the mountain magically grew in height, making the task more and more arduous for them. When they finally reached the peak after nine days and ten nights, Kaushiki was nowhere to be seen. Turning back, Raktabeeja saw her astride her lion, far below in the battlefield, mocking him with her laughter.

'Is this how you'll fight with me? With magic instead of valour?' he roared. 'Then watch me as I come to get you and drag you by your hair to Shumbha's palace.'

Enraged at his temerity, Kaushiki plunged into battle with Raktabeeja and his army. As the fight became fiercer, seven more goddesses emerged from her. Vaishnavi attacked the danava army with her discus, Aindri with her thunderbolt, Kaumari with her lance, Varahi with her sword, Brahmani

with her taravaari (also a type of sword), Narasimhika with
her sharp claws and Maheshwari with her trident.

The danavas ran helter-skelter to save themselves, but
Raktabeeja fought on without a care. Pleased with his years
of severe penance, Brahma had granted him the boon that
wherever his rakta (blood) fell on the ground, it would take
the form of a beeja (seed) and from it would immediately
sprout another Raktabeeja, who too would possess the same
magical power as him. So, every time a sword slashed him or
a trident pierced him on the battlefield, his blood would drop
to the ground and lo and behold, a new Raktabeeja would
spring up!

Aware of his magical ability, the goddesses ceaselessly
continued to fight the asura army, careful not to hurt
Raktabeeja, until Aindri unknowingly struck him on his
head with her thunderbolt. As blood gushed out of his
head, tens of thousands of Raktabeejas, full of strength and
brutality, emerged and joined the battle against Kaushiki.
Even as the goddesses looked on, the whole world was filled
with asuras.

The devas trembled from their hiding place. 'Will Devi
Kaushiki be able to defeat Raktabeeja?' was the doubt in all
their minds.

A similar thought occurred to Kaushiki. What could she
do to stop Raktabeeja from multiplying? Then, closing her
eyes, she summoned Kali once again. 'Go forth, Kali and do
what is to be done!' she commanded.

And so, Kali opened her mouth wide until one lip touched
the skies and the other touched the ground. And even as the

seven goddesses wounded Raktabeeja with their weapons, Kali stretched her enormous tongue and licked up every drop of blood pouring from his body until there was no more blood in him. She then pulled him and every last one of his replicates into her gaping mouth and devoured them, thus annihilating the fearsome demon.

Note

An akshouhini is a battle formation that comprises 10,9350 foot soldiers, 65,510 horsemen, 2,1870 charioteers and 2,1870 elephant riders.

According to scholars, Raktabeeja symbolizes our thoughts of lethargy, arrogance, violence and untruthfulness. These thoughts need but a small opportunity to emerge as completely new, separate and powerful entities and attack and harass us and others with the same force as the original thought—not weakening a wee bit but multiplying infinitely.

After the slaying of Raktabeeja, Shumbha and Nishumbha, the descendants of the notorious asura Hiranyakashipu, set out to face Kaushiki. Towards the end of the ferocious battle that followed, Kaushiki threw Nishumbha to the ground and felled him with a torrent of arrows.

Enraged, Shumbha expanded his body to cover the entire sky and, with his eight hands armed with eight different magical weapons, he swooped down to attack her. Deciding that the time had come to vanquish the impudent asura, Kaushiki blew her conch and pierced Shumbha's heart with her trident. As he fell to the ground, the mountains shook, the earth trembled and the rivers and oceans overflowed momentarily before all was peaceful once again.

11

Gaja

When the dreaded Mahisha was vanquished by Durga, the morale of the entire asura clan was shaken. At the same time, many of his relatives, friends and followers were consumed with the idea of avenging his death. Amongst these were Mahishi, his sister, Raktabeeja, his military general and Gaja, his son. However, Gaja was only a teenager when his father was killed. How could such a young boy fight the Goddess and hope to win?

�֍

Gaja, the elephant-headed son of Mahisha, was struck with grief. His father had been killed by Devi after nine days and nine nights of intense battle.

'I want to avenge my father! Tell me, O Guru, how can I go about it?' a helpless Gaja asked Shukracharya, the Guru of the Asuras. 'My father has trained me in all the skills required for battle. Moreover, he has taught me never to bow down to the might of others, never to lose faith in my own supremacy. I must live by his words; I must avenge his death!'

'Patience, Gaja,' Shukracharya said softly. 'It is not wise to act in haste. Our army is still reeling from Mahisha's death and its crushing defeat. We need to give them time to recover. And you need to give yourself time to grow up. If a warrior as great as your father was vanquished by Devi, how can you expect to win against her?'

Gaja was crestfallen. What Gurudev said was true, but how could he not do anything...wouldn't that be cowardice?

Reading his thoughts, Shukracharya said, 'It is not cowardice, but wisdom, Gaja. And I am not asking you to sit in your palace and grieve either. Go to the mountains and pray to Brahma. He is easy to please and when he appears before you, ask for a boon that will help you avenge your father.'

So, discarding the riches and luxuries of his palace, Gaja set out barefoot towards the mountains. Once there, he climbed to the highest peak and, standing on his toes with arms outstretched in prayer above his head, he started to pray to Brahma. Hundreds of years passed by, but Gaja continued to pray without a care for the extreme heat, cold and rains that alternated around him; instead, such was the power of his penance that it caused his entire body to heat up and catch fire. The fire soon spread through the three worlds, scorching the planets, ocean waters and even the sun.

Unable to bear the blistering heat, the devas begged Brahma to appear before Gaja, but Brahma was reluctant.

'Gaja is seething from the death of his father. If I appear before him now, he will ask for a boon that I cannot refuse. In all probability, it will be something that will bring harm to the universe. Let me test him some more; let us wait for a hundred more years,' Brahma advised.

The devas, however, were impatient. 'O Brahma, we cannot tolerate this singeing heat for another hundred years; the intensity of this heat will only grow stronger with each passing year and we will perish before his penance is completed. Please appear before him and grant him his wish,' they beseeched.

Brahma smiled. He could foresee the future and was amused at the naivety of the devas. 'Very well,' he said, 'you have chosen to relieve yourself of a small but immediate hardship knowing well that it will lead to a graver problem in the future. So be it!' He then appeared before Gaja and offered to grant his boon.

'O Brahma, you have finally arrived! I bow to you and ask for the boon of immortality,' Gaja replied.

'That is not possible, Gaja. Ask for endless wealth and prosperity, great power and strength or even spiritual riches... I can grant you anything but immortality, for every being that is born into this world must die.'

'In that case, O Brahma, grant me the boon that I may

be invincible in war and be killed by only that being who has never lusted after worldly pleasures,' Gaja said.

'So be it,' said Brahma and returned to his abode. The fire engulfing the universe immediately disappeared and all was back to normal. The devas heaved a huge sigh of relief. However, their respite was short-lived, for Gaja had already started preparing for a great war.

Soon, bringing together all the great asura kings and their armies, Gaja attacked Devaloka and captured it. Dethroning Indra, he established his rule over the three worlds and began to torture the devas and the sages for their compliance in his father's death. Disrupting the prayers and yagnas of the sages, he forced them to worship him instead. 'There is none greater than me in this universe,' he roared, 'so stop worshipping Brahma, Vishnu and Shiva for even they are nothing but ants that will be crushed under my feet when the time comes!'

However, the sages in the holy city of Kashi on Bhuloka refused to bow down to him. 'There is none greater than Shiva and we shall not worship anyone but him, even if it means death to us!' they proclaimed.

The remark infuriated Gaja. 'Where is this Shiva?' he thundered. 'I shall confront him and settle the matter once and for all! I shall drive him out of this very Kashi that seems to be his abode.'

He then put together an army of ferocious asura warriors and set out for Kashi. However, in the battle that ensued, they were no match for Shiva's army of ganas and were soon on the verge of defeat. Enraged, Gaja decided to enter the battle himself. Plucking the string of his bow, sending an enormous tremor through the three worlds, he challenged Shiva to a duel.

When Shiva heard Gaja's words though, he let out a laugh. 'Stop before it is too late, Gaja,' he warned. 'There isn't an arrow in this universe that can touch me, let alone cause me harm! Drop your naivety and return to your abode. Let those who worship me do so in peace.'

Shiva's words only added to Gaja's fury. He strung his bow and sent an arrow piercing the air towards Shiva, but the arrow burnt to ashes before reaching its target. Gaja then sent arrow after arrow towards Shiva; all of them met with a similar fate, not causing as much as a scratch on Shiva. Blinded by rage, he rushed towards Shiva with his sword, but before he knew it, Shiva was on top of him, driving his trident into his body.

As death stared at his face, Gaja invoked Brahma. 'You had granted me the boon that I couldn't be killed by any being who has submitted to the lust of worldly pleasures and yet, Shiva has slain me! How can it be?' he asked.

'O Gaja, your arrogance hasn't left you even at the time of your death! Open your eyes and see...for before you stands Shiva, who has known no lust for anything in this universe. With no worldly attachments and no desire for luxuries, he is the greatest Vairagi of all. Clad in nothing but a tiger skin and adorned with not gold and silver but ashes, snakes and the humble Rudraksha beads, he is the epitome of detachment. So, I have not failed you, Gaja; rather, you have met death in exactly the manner you wished for! And what's more, your father was amongst the greatest devotees of Shiva, for from his throat had emerged a Shivalinga when he was slain.'

Hearing Brahma's words, Gaja realized his folly. Turning to Shiva, he asked to be pardoned for his arrogance. 'O Shiva,' he said, 'I am blessed to have met my end at your hands. However, please grant me a dying wish. Please accept this elephant hide of mine as a cloak to cover you always. It has withstood the burning of my body during my penance and this way, I can forever remain close to you.'

'So be it,' said Shiva, placing his palm on Gaja's forehead. 'And henceforth, I shall also be known as Kritivassas or "one who wears an elephant hide".'

Then, as Shiva lifted the hide to cover himself, Gaja closed his eyes and attained salvation.

Note

According to another version of the story, the intense battle with Gaja and the subsequent slaying of the demon left Shiva in a state of agitated trance. Having lost control of his senses, he dragged Gaja's body to the forest, mercilessly ripped off the elephant skin, wrapped it around himself and danced like a drunk, ignorant of the fact that Parvati and little Kartikeya too were in the forest. Upon seeing this fierce form of his father, Kartikeya trembled with fear and clung on to Parvati, who tried to reassure her son despite being frightened herself.

This entire scene later became famous as the Gajaasurasamhara (slayer of Gajaasura) pose and can be found carved, down to the detail of Parvati pacifying Kartikeya, in several temples in South India, especially the ones built by the Chola kings, as they were great devotees of Shiva. In fact, some versions of the Gajaasura story locate the battle not in Varanasi but in Valuvur in Tamil Nadu, where the Cholas have built a temple to commemorate this glorious triumph of Shiva.

12

Dashagriva

We saw earlier that Hayagriva was a horse-headed demon; so, figuring out that Dashagriva refers to a ten-headed being is no rocket science. And who else could a ten-headed being be other than Ravana? But Ravana wasn't the name he was given at birth; it was the name given to him by...well, why don't you read on and find out?

'**O**m Brahmaya Namaha. Om Brahmaya Namaha. Om Brahmaya Namaha.'

The sound of Dashagriva's chants reverberated through the three worlds. Ten thousand years had passed since he started his penance deep in the forests, along with his brothers Kumbhakarna and Vibheeshana. Surviving without a morsel of food, he cut off one of his ten heads every thousand years and offered it to the sacred fire to appease Brahma. Only one head remained on his shoulders now and as he got ready to sacrifice it, Brahma appeared before him.

'O Dashagriva, you have performed a penance that is unmatched by any being! Ask me for any boon and I shall grant you that.'

Dashagriva was pleased. His extreme penance had borne fruit. Growing up under the tutelage of his father, Sage Visravas, he had gained all knowledge contained in the Vedas and Upanishads and had mastered the craft of war. His father had also taught him to appreciate the arts and play the veena flawlessly. However, it wasn't his Brahmin lineage that appealed to Dashagriva. His grandfather, the daitya king Sumali, had instilled in him a far greater love for strength and power and it was to fulfil his thirst for invincibility and immortality that Dashagriva had started the penance.

'O Brahma, I wish to be immortal,' Dashagriva said, his hands folded in humility.

'Son, I cannot grant you that. Know that even I, the Creator, am not free from the cycle of birth and death; so ask for another boon,' Brahma replied.

'Then let it be that death comes to me at the hands of anyone but a deva, danava, daitya, yaksha, rakshasa, naga, vanara, pakshi or indeed any god!' Dashagriva requested, pleased with his cleverness.

Brahma smiled. 'So be it,' he said, 'and because of your devotion, I also grant you back the heads you offered to the sacred fire with the boon that every time your head is cut in battle, a new head will spring forth and take its place.'

Even as Brahma spoke thus, Dashagriva's nine heads returned to him. Before disappearing, Brahma also granted Kumbhakarna the boon that he could sleep for several years at a stretch and Vibheeshana that he would be able to choose the path of righteousness at every stage in his life.

Upon returning home, Dashagriva was welcomed by his grandfather, Sumali, who took him under his wings and trained him to be a powerful but just king.

'Grandfather, I shall no doubt become king after you, but where should I rule from? Where shall I establish my kingdom, for you know that I cannot reside in Patala. I was born on earth and I am meant to rule over it,' Dashagriva asked Sumali.

'Indeed, Son, you shall rule the earth and you shall rule it from the most beautiful city on its surface,' Sumali replied. 'Dashagriva, you shall rule from none other than the Golden Lanka!'

Dashagriva was astounded with his grandfather's pronouncement. 'Lanka does not belong to me, Grandfather! It belongs to Vaishravana (or Kubera), my half-brother.'

'Indeed, Kubera rules over Lanka now; but, Son, it wasn't always thus. Amongst the peaks of the island mountain of Trikuta lies a rock with its four sides chiselled so steep that even a bird cannot reach it. This is where Lanka was built by Vishwakarma, the divine architect, for me and my brothers Mali and Malyavan. O Dashagriva, we lived with our wives and children and established our kingdom in that Lanka of a thousand golden houses that matched the splendour of Indra's Amarawati in Devaloka, and we ruled our people justly and worshipped Shiva with all our hearts,' Sumali recounted.

'Then how did Vaishravana get possession of Lanka, Grandfather?' Dashagriva asked, curious and agitated.

'The devas were afraid of us, Son, and they plotted our death with Vishnu. In a battle that raged for hundreds of years, your grand uncles Mali and Malyavan were killed by Vishnu and although I escaped that fate, I had to leave Lanka and establish my kingdom in Patala. It was then that your father gifted Vaishravana, his first born, with the city of Lanka along with his magical vehicle, the Pushpaka Vimana. Son, I am only asking you to take back what is ours. So, use your skills of diplomacy or appeasement or war on your half-brother, but take back Lanka!'

Dashagriva seethed with anger. 'I shall do your bidding, Grandfather!' he said and summoned his messenger Prahasta.

'Go forth, Prahasta, and let Vaishravana know that I am laying claim on what is rightfully mine—the city of Lanka! Remind him of his wisdom and ask him to follow the righteous path by returning Lanka to the rakshasas.'

Upon hearing Prashasta, Vaishravana was in a dilemma. He went to his father, who advised him to leave Lanka and establish his kingdom close to Mount Kailasa. 'Dashagriva has been granted boons that make him invincible and perhaps immortal too. His pride and arrogance will cause his downfall one day but until then, only a fool will make an enemy out of him. Give him what he wants.'

And so, Vaishravana left Lanka with his people, making

way for Dashagriva to enter the golden city in pomp and be crowned the King of Rakshasas. He ruled over his people justly and his people adored their king, but the devas and sages were terrified, for, like his grandfather, Dashagriva too took pleasure in harassing them. When, hearing about his atrocities, Vaishravana sent an emissary to advise him to change his ways, Dashagriva was enraged. He gathered an army of the mightiest rakshasas and asuras and attacked Vaishravana.

In the ferocious battle that followed, he defeated his half-brother and looted and plundered his kingdom. Amongst the precious things he took away from Vaishravana as a sign of victory was the Puspaka Vimana, the flying chariot. Built by Vishwakarma, the chariot was supported by golden pillars, had precious stones embedded in the doors and windows and held blossoming fruit trees of every sort growing within its seemingly small enclosure!

Mounting the chariot, Dashagriva started his journey back to Lanka. However, upon reaching the vicinity of a mountain covered with thick forests, the chariot came to a screeching halt.

'What could be on this mountain that this chariot, which moves according to the wishes of its owner, has suddenly stopped?' Dashagriva wondered. Embarrassed that the chariot refused to budge despite his command even as his ministers looked on, Dashagriva landed it at the foot of the mountain and stepped out.

'This mountain dares to obstruct my journey; now see how I uproot it and throw it to the side!' he thundered in a rage that brought even the devas out of their abode. Then, sitting on his hunches, Dashagriva conjured eighteen more arms and picked up the mountain along with all the trees, animals and birds that inhabited it. It was a sight that made the rakshasa army smile in delight. However, the devas shuddered, for the mountain was none other than Kailasa, the abode of Shiva himself.

Sitting atop Kailasa, Shiva and Parvati felt the mountain tremble as it was being uprooted. Parvati looked at her husband questioningly, but Shiva only smiled and pressed his little toe to the ground. Kailasa immediately sank back to the ground, squashing the mighty Dashagriva under it and causing him to let out a scream that reverberated across the three worlds. It was then that he saw Nandi, the leader of Shiva's ganas, wandering in the vicinity and realized his folly.

Like his grandfather Sumali, Dashagriva too had been an ardent devotee of Shiva all his life. He now felt ashamed that he, steeped in his arrogance, hadn't been able to recognize Shiva's abode. Full of remorse, he cut open his chest and, plucking his nerves, used them as strings to play the veena as he sang songs eulogizing Shiva.

Dashagriva lay thus, crushed under Kailasa but singing praises of Shiva for a hundred years before Shiva decided that he had been punished enough. He gently pulled back his toe and relieved the pressure on his devotee, who immediately started to scale the Kailasa so he could fall at Shiva's feet and ask to be pardoned.

'O Dashagriva, I am pleased with your devotion and your resilience. Know now that you will forever be counted amongst my greatest devotees,' said Shiva, 'and since your terrifying roar of pain made the three worlds cry, you shall henceforth be known as Ravana!'

Thus, Dashagriva returned to Lanka with a new name and ruled from there for hundreds of years before Vishnu descended on earth to be born as Rama.

Note

Remember Dashagriva being crushed under Kailasa? It is said that such was his devotion for Shiva that even under such great agony, he composed the 'Shiva Tandava Stotram', all 1008 verses of it, and sang it for a hundred years. The song describes Shiva as he dances the Tandava Nritya—how his hair moves, how the water of river Ganga splashes around, how his drums sound, how his ornaments move along with him and so on.

Scholars who have closely studied Ravana closely say that although he was undoubtedly the greatest devotee of Shiva, he never really understood Shiva. For Shiva is the embodiment of 'vairagya' or the principle of detachment, whereas Ravana was the epitome of attachment; he craved for worldly pleasures and luxuries and thought it right to snatch whatever his heart desired and make it his own—be it Lanka, the Pushpaka Vimana or Sita herself. Despite knowing the Vedas and Upanishads, he never really 'knew' them or understood their essence.

13

Tataka

Suketu, a childless yaksha king, did severe penance and prayed to Brahma for several years. Pleased, Brahma bestowed him with a beautiful and intelligent daughter, Tataka, who possessed the strength of a thousand elephants. Yet, when Rama and Lakshmana encountered her in the forests on the banks of the Sarayu River, Tataka was a grotesque man-eating demoness. How did this transformation come to be?

❖

After Indra had killed Vritra, the devas brought him down to Bhuloka to wash away from his body the sin of having killed a Brahmana. After bathing in the waters of the Sarayu, Indra was cleansed of all impurities and gladdened by the generosity of the river that had absorbed his sins into herself, he blessed her and the surrounding forests.

'O Sarayu, these provinces on your banks that bear the impurity of my body shall become prosperous and attain fame in the world as the cities of Malada and Karusha.'

True to Indra's blessings, the provinces began to flourish and people from all over came down to live there. After several years, Sage Agastya too arrived at the banks of the river and set up his ashram there. Once, when performing yagna along with his disciples, the rakshasa Sunda wandered into the ashram in an intoxicated state and attacked them. Furious, Agastya closed his eyes and, by the sheer power of his meditation, burnt Sunda to death.

Upon hearing about her husband's death, Tataka was besides herself with rage. Along with her sons Mareecha and Subahu, she attacked Agastya, who, in turn, cursed the three of them.

'O Yakshini, you shall henceforth give up your beauty and instead repulse people with your looks. I curse you to become a hideous man-eating demoness! And as for your sons, they too shall be transformed into demonic rakshasas,' Agastya declared.

Tataka was distraught. Not only had she lost her husband, she had now transformed into a monstrous being. Not knowing what to do, she went to Patala with her sons to seek the aid of Sumali, the patriarch of rakshasas.

'Go to Lanka and explain your plight to Ravana, my grandson; he shall surely help the widow of a fellow rakshasa!' Sumali advised.

Sure enough, Ravana helped Tataka capture Malada and Karusha after which she burnt down the cities and turned the beautiful land into a dense forest that became home to her and her sons. With rounded shoulders, oversized heads, cavernous mouths and gigantic bodies, Tataka, Mareecha and Subahu terrorized people living on the outskirts of the forest and devoured anyone who dared to venture within. Such was their tyranny that even the sun and clouds did not dare break through the dense foliage of trees and enter the dark bowels of the forest. Not surprisingly, no animal or bird inhabited the forest except for dreadful insects that crept and crawled in the darkness.

Moreover, nursing a particular hatred towards the sages, Mareecha and Subahu spared no opportunity to harass them by throwing blood, flesh and bones into the sacrificial fire, destroying the sanctity of their yagnas.

Several years passed before one day, Sage Vishwamitra approached King Dasharatha for help. He was planning to conduct an important yagna at his ashram on the banks of the Sarayu and, seeking protection from the rakshasas, asked Dasharatha to send Rama with him to stand guard during the sacred ritual. Rama was then only a sixteen-year-old boy, and the king wasn't sure about sending him to confront demons with magical powers; but the sage was adamant.

'I would rather take your young son as my protector than your entire army!' Sage Vishwamitra proclaimed.

After much persuasion by the sage as well as his royal advisor Sage Vashishtha, Dasharatha finally agreed to send both Rama and his brother Lakshmana with Vishwamitra. Soon, they reached the banks of the Sarayu, where the sage taught the princes two mantras, chanting which would make them invincible as well as protect them from hunger and fatigue. He also narrated the story of how Tataka and her sons came to be the monstrous beings they now were. Listening to the story, Rama had several questions; he wasn't sure it was right to kill the demoness and so decided in his mind to maim her instead.

Upon reaching the forest, Rama and Lakshmana braved through the tangled overgrowth all around them and searched for the cave where Tataka rested. Despite it being broad daylight outside, there was nothing but darkness and the cacophonous sounds of a thousand insects surrounding them. After long, when they finally reached the cave, Rama took the bow off his shoulder and twanged its string, causing the entire forest to resonate with its sound.

'What is that sound?' a thunderous growl came from within the cave. 'And who is it that dares set foot in my forest without my permission?'

As she emerged from her cave, Tataka saw Rama and Lakshmana standing afar with bows in their hands. Tall as a hill herself, the sight of the brothers' tiny frames made her roar with laughter.

'Go away you fools or I shall eat you up and spit out your

bones in no time!' she said.

But when the brothers did not budge, Tataka was furious. With her nostrils breathing fire, she charged towards her prey, swinging her arms wildly and flinging leaves and sand from the forest floor at them so that they were covered by a massive cloud of dust. The entire forest started to tremble and outside, the sages and their disciples cringed in their ashrams, fearing the worst.

When the dust finally settled, clearing Rama's vision, he aimed an arrow at Tataka, who was almost upon him. Enraged, the rakshasi sent out an ear-shattering scream that reverberated through the forest. Using her magical powers, she sent a rain of rocks and boulders crashing down on Rama and Lakshmana and even as they looked for cover, Tataka uprooted trees and hurled them towards the brothers. Soon, she was appearing and disappearing from their view, changing her form at will and creating illusions to confuse them.

Worried, Vishwamitra spoke up, 'O Rama, enough is your compassion! Do not bide your time, for Tataka is a yakshini and rakshasi; her powers will grow manifold once the sun sets and you would be no match for her then!'

Rama nodded. Realizing that it wouldn't be enough to maim a rakshasi who possessed such great magical powers—he had already cut off her hands while Lakshmana had lopped her ears and the tip of her nose—he picked up his bow and once again aimed an arrow at her. This time, the arrow went piercing into Tataka's chest and she dropped dead on the forest floor.

Note

Almost immediately after Tataka had been killed, the forest, which had been a place of gloom and dread since hundreds of years, was bathed in sunlight. Trees began to flower and birds and animals started to return to what had once been their home. Rama and Lakshmana then proceeded to the ashram with Sage Vishwamitra, who, pleased with Rama, gave him mantras to conjure divine weapons such as the Danda Chakra, Dharma Chakra, Kaala Chakra, Vishnu Chakra, Indra Chakra, Trishula, Dharma Paasha, Varuna Paasha, Kaala Paasha, Varunastra, Pinakastra, Narayanastra, the formidable Brahmastra and several others.

Thereafter, the brothers stood guard as Vishwamitra performed the yagna with his disciples. As soon as Mareecha and Subahu appeared from the skies with blood, bones and animal carcasses to drop into the fire, Rama conjured the Agneyastra and sent it towards Subahu, burning him to death. As for Mareecha, Rama invoked the Manavastra, which hit the rakshasa on his chest with the power of a hundred lightning bolts, and sent him flying into the air until he fell into the sea and sank to the bottom.

Mareecha did not die though. He lived for a few more years until, in the guise of a golden deer, he encountered Rama once again in the Dandaka forest and lured him away from Sita so Ravana could kidnap her.

14

Kabandha

Brahma had always denied the boon of immortality to any of the asuras who prayed to him, no matter how extreme their penances. However, there was one being to whom he did grant that boon. Who was this being and what did he do with such a powerful boon? Let's find out.

Vishwavasu, son of the Gandharva king Sri, was happy with his life. Descendants of Sage Kashyap and Devi Arishtha, the Gandharvas were born to be one with nature and music. Living in their own domain, the Gandharvaloka, they were supremely handsome and served as divine healers or musicians in Indra's court whenever they were called upon. At other times, they lived a life of leisure, dallying in the forests with their wives, the beautiful apsaras.

Once, Sage Ashtavakra happened to pass through the forest glade where Vishwavasu was relaxing. Seeing the sage, whose body was severely bent at eight different places (hence the name, 'ashta' meaning 'eight' and 'vakra' meaning 'bend') hobbling along, Vishwavasu let out a booming laugh.

Enraged, Ashtavakra said, 'O Gandharva! You are so consumed by your own handsome self that you have forgotten what it is to respect others. For this, I curse you that a day will come when you will be transformed into an ugly demon!'

Several years passed after this incident and Vishwavasu forgot about the curse. One day, though, when watching his wife Menaka dance with the other apsaras, a disturbing thought crossed Vishwavasu's mind. 'What if I am not able to enjoy these pleasures for long? What if I die sometime soon?' Distressed, he decided to pray to Brahma to ensure a long life for himself.

Pleased with the tough penance he performed for several years, Brahma appeared before Vishwavasu and to his surprise, granted him the boon of immortality. Soon, the realization that he would never die made the Gandharva more and more arrogant. Vile thoughts invaded his mind and made him question Indra's authority.

'Why should I entertain Indra when I too am immortal like him now? Indeed, I am his equal, not subservient to him anymore!' Vishwavasu thought to himself.

He then headed for Devaloka and challenged Indra

to a duel. In the fight that followed, Indra hit him with his thunderbolt, the Vajra, causing Vishwavasu's head and thighs to withdraw into his body. The powerful strike jolted the gandharva back to reality and upon realizing the consequence of his behaviour, he became dejected.

'O Indra! Pardon me my conceit. I have realized my mistake and regret it deeply. But tell me, now that I am the way I am, with no head or legs, how will I eat and how will I move around? Please lead me to Yama's hell... I would rather die than live in this grotesque body!' he begged.

Indra smiled. 'I am glad you've realized your folly. You have the boon of immortality and so you will have to live; but since you are one of us and have been dear to us thus far, I will help you with your predicament.' So saying, he caused Vishwavasu's arms to grow as long as a hundred yojanas and placed a single eye, nose and mouth on his stomach. He then continued, 'Since it is I who have brought this fate upon you, let me tell you this—you shall regain your original form the day Rama and his brother Lakshmana hack off these arms of yours. Until then, you shall be known to all as Kabandha, the torso without a head.'

After Indra vanished, Kabandha descended to Bhuloka and started living in the forests near the Krauncha mountains. Gigantic as a mountain and dark as a black cloud, he would wander about hunting for food all day, and upon spotting a lion or elephant or tiger with his fiery yellow eye, he would haul it with his long arms and devour it using his enormous fanged mouth. His appearance scared not only the animals and birds but also the sages and their disciples passing through the forest. With nothing much to do, he started harassing these sages by visiting their ashrams on the outskirts of the forest and obstructing their yagnas. Soon, he came to be known as Rakshasa Kabandha.

Hundreds of years passed with Kabandha continuing to live in his demonic form and tormenting all beings around him until one day, Rama and Lakshmana entered the Krauncha forest in search of Sita. Jatayu had informed them that Ravana had kidnapped Sita and flown southwards on his Pushpaka Vimana, but there was no way to know where he had taken her. So, leaving the Dandaka forest behind them during their search, they walked towards Sage Matanga's ashram in the south, hoping to find someone who could give them more information.

Upon reaching the foothills of the Krauncha mountains, they saw in front of them a thick, impassable forest covered with innumerable creepers and gigantic trees whose dense foliage prevented sunlight from seeping in. As they slowly progressed through the darkness encompassing them, they heard a low rumble that gradually grew louder and louder until it turned into an unbearable ear-piercing roar. Both Rama and Lakshmana grew alert and brought out their bows and arrows, ready to confront whatever lay ahead of them. However, Kabandha was too quick for them. Before they could make out his grotesque form in the darkness, his long arms had swooped them off the ground and made them his prisoners. With Rama firmly lodged in one palm and Lakshmana in the other, he gave out a thunderous laugh.

'Hunger! There is nothing more horrible in this world than hunger!' he bellowed. 'Ever since I remember, I have been ravenously hungry and no matter how much I eat—bears, elephants, lions, tigers, boars and what not—I only feel more and more hungry. And what do I have with me now... two wretched humans! Will they satiate my hunger? No! But I must eat them, because as long as my hunger exists, I cannot think straight; I cannot think of anything else!'

However, just as he was about to bring his palms to his mouth to devour Rama and Lakshmana, the brothers brought out their swords and hacked off Kabandha's arms at the shoulders. His torso immediately fell to the ground with a thud, sending tremors through the forest. With blood streaming out of his amputated body and his arms lying lifeless on the forest floor, Kabandha let out an ear-shattering howl.

'Who are you?' he asked his assailants even as he writhed in pain.

'This here, in front of you, is Rama, the successor of the Ikshavaku dynasty and I am his younger brother,' replied Lakshmana.

Kabandha's happiness knew no bounds when he heard Lakshmana's words. 'O Rama, you are finally here! I have waited for the two of you for hundreds of years. Blessed am I that you have come and cut off my arms!' Then narrating his tale to the two brothers, he asked them to dig a pit and burn his torso in it.

'No, Kabandha. We cannot live with the sin of burning you!' replied Rama. 'We cut off your arms to save ourselves and the only reason we wanted to save ourselves was so we could find Sita, who has been kidnapped by Ravana. Tell us, have you seen or heard anything that could help us find her?'

Kabandha's eye drooped in desolation. 'Only when I am relieved of this body that knows nothing but hunger can I think of anything else. So, please burn me, O brave brothers. Please!' he begged.

Listening to his desperate pleas, Rama and Lakshmana dug a pit on the forest floor and throwing Kabandha's amputated torso in, set it on fire. No sooner had they done that than a golden spark emanated from Kabandha's body and shot up into the sky. When it dropped back to the ground, it was no longer a spark but the Gandharva Vishwavasu.

Dressed in radiant white garments and adorned with several ornaments and garlands, Vishwavasu folded his hands and bowed. 'I am forever indebted to you for releasing me from my wretched rakshasa body,' he said, elated. 'And now, listen carefully to what I say since this is the only way you can get to Sita. Only a person who is in a state as desperate as yours, O Rama, can help you in your mission. Go forth, find this person and befriend him.'

'But who is this person? And where do we find him?' asked Rama.

'He whom you seek is not an ordinary person; he is a courageous monkey, Sugriva, who has travelled all across the world and knows exactly what place lies where. What is more, he has also lost his wife just like you and has been banished from his kingdom. You will find him hiding in the Rishyamukha mountains; go help him regain his kingdom and he will surely help you reunite with Sita!'

Then, Vishwavasu bowed down to the brothers and, thanking them once again for releasing him from the curse, vanished into the vastness of the sky.

Note

Sometimes, our arrogance and ego put us in situations where even the thing we most desire becomes an unbearable burden—in Vishwavasu's case, it was his immortality. We then have to wait for someone to come along and share their wisdom so that our intellect goes back to its normal state. In some cases, this wait can in itself be unbearably long. Perhaps this is nature's way of testing our patience while we discover our true selves.

While the Aadhyatma Ramayana identifies the sage whom Vishwavasu angered as Ashtavakra, Valmiki Ramayana's Aranyakanda identifies him as Sthoolashira. The latter text describes Vishwavasu playing pranks on sages and their disciples by changing himself into a hideous demon. When he tried the same with Sthoolashira, he was cursed to live as an ugly demon for the rest of his life.

Before the encounter with Kabandha, Rama, Lakshmana and Sita had passed through the Dandaka forest, where an equally grotesque demon, Viradha, had captured Sita. Viradha too had been a Gandharva named Tumburu earlier and had been cursed by Kubera to live the life of a demon. He has been described as a gigantic rakshasa with hollow green eyes, bristly red hair all over his body and a mouth that stretched from one javelin-like ear to the other. When Rama first laid eyes on him, Viradha carried Sita in one hand and in the other he held a metal rod that had skewered on it three dead lions, four tigers, two wolves, ten spotted dear and the bloody head of an elephant. Having been granted the boon of invincibility against all weapons, Rama and Lakshmana were unable to hurt him with arrows. Instead, they had to break his limbs one by one and bury him alive.

Scholars have interpreted Kabandha's and Viradha's deformity as being the deformity of the mind or thoughts. Irrespective of who you are born as, your thoughts are what shape you and make you either a deva or a rakshasa.

15

Trijata

Many a time, you are slotted as being a certain kind of person because you were born into a particular family. If you're familiar with the caste system as it exists today, for instance, you will know that people are considered to be 'filthy' and 'untouchable' if they are born into a family of sweepers and 'wise' if they are born to highly educated parents...and I hope you know this is wrong. In fact, there was one rakshasi who defied this kind of stereotyping and made a place for herself amongst the very few venerated demons in Hindu mythology. You might also be surprised to know that today, she is known more for her dreams, referred to as Trijata Swapna, than her lineage. Do you want to know what she dreamt of? Then read on...

✧

Trijata twitched and turned in her sleep. Even sleep, it seemed, was punishing her, giving her visions that made her restless rather than allowing her mind some peace. The vision she had just had, though, was both disturbing and reassuring. Disturbing, because she was staunchly loyal to her king, Ravana, and reassuring because, in secret, she admired Rama.

'What fault is it of mine that I've been born a rakshasi? Why should I suffer for the transgressions of Ravana?' she asked herself, getting up to stretch her limbs.

As the light of the moon washed the expanse of Ashoka Vatika, Ravana's mesmerizing royal garden that had been designed by Vishwakarma himself, she could see Sita curled up not very far away. Like herself, sleep seemed to have deserted Sita too, for she was weeping, craving to return to Rama. It would soon be morning and the rakshasis posted on her vigil would start harassing her afresh. Ravana's order to all the rakshasis was to convince Sita to marry him.

'Why?' Trijata wondered. 'Why does the Lord want to marry someone else's wife? It does not become him to act thus!' But there was nothing she could do. Letting out a sigh, she tried to go back to sleep, but the vision refused to leave her.

When the first rays of the morning sun pierced through the canopy of trees, the legion of rakshasis descended on Sita once again—some pulling her hair, some poking her with the blunt side of their spears, some using foul language to intimidate her.

'There is no one as strong and intelligent as our king in

the whole world,' said one of them.

'You should be glad he wants to make you his wife; he will be a far better match than that wretched Rama, who does nothing but wander in the forests and give you a pathetic little hut to stay in. And yet, you reject our Lord's proposal, the arrogant fool that you are!' sneered another.

'Look at your clothes! What tatters your husband has provided you with! Marry our king and he'll bedeck you with the richest of clothes and the most beautiful of ornaments. You will live in the luxury you truly deserve!' boasted the third.

After going through the trauma of being tricked and abducted by Ravana in the guise of a brahmin, Sita had held herself together for a while, hoping that Rama would come to her rescue. But days had turned to weeks and it was now over ten months since she entered Ashoka Vatika as Ravana's prisoner; she was now losing hope with each passing day. Even as Sita cowered and wept, the rakshasis persisted. 'Marry our king, marry our king,' they chorused.

Trijata watched it all with a heavy heart. Only a few days back, when Sita had told Ravana that she'd never think of marrying him when her husband was still alive, Ravana had used his powers of illusion to show her the severed heads of Rama and Lakshmana. Knowing her master's trickery, she had tried to assure an inconsolable Sita that her husband was safe. Yet, unable to bear Ravana's insults and feeling abandoned by Rama, Sita had asked her to gather firewood so she could burn in a pyre. Trijata avoided doing so, giving some excuse or the other.

Now, hearing the taunts of her fellow rakshasis, she wondered how long it would be before Sita tried to kill herself again. 'And what if she does not tell me this time? What if she gives up her life without my knowing? I will not be able to live with that!' she thought.

'Stop it, you imbeciles!' Trijata's roar took the rakshasis by surprise. 'Stop troubling Sita or only woes will come your way!'

'What do you mean?' the other rakshasis asked, turning to face Trijata. They knew she wasn't as aggressive as a rakshasi was meant to be, but respected her for her age and wisdom.

'Last night, I had a vision. I saw a monkey burning down our beautiful Lanka and our rakshasa clan being killed by Rama's army. I saw Rama, dressed in resplendent white clothes and shining like the sun, come to Lanka and carry Sita away on a white elephant. And I saw our king Ravana, drenched in oil, riding a donkey in the direction of south!'

The last statement sent a shiver among the rakshasis. They knew that Trijata had visions that came true and they were also aware that riding in the direction of south meant riding towards Yama, the God of Death. Could this be true? Could their impregnable Lanka be burnt down and their lord and master killed? It seemed too farfetched to believe. So, they laughed off the matter saying Trijata was growing old and senile. For the time being though, they decided to leave Sita alone and turned their attention to other chores.

Unknown to them, hiding among the leaves of a tree, Hanuman sat listening to every word spoken by Trijata. His task had been to meet Sita and convey the message that Rama was on his way to rescue her; but now, he began to wonder. 'If Trijata's vision is true, perhaps I am the one destined to burn down Lanka? Perhaps I should complete that task first?' And so, he jumped across Ashok Vatika and entered Ravana's palace.

By twilight, Lanka was in flames, just as Trijata had predicted! With his tail set afire on Ravana's orders, Hanuman had hopped all over the city, setting everything that came in his way on fire. At Ashok Vatika, as the rakshasis ran helter-skelter upon hearing the terrifying news, Hanuman quietly doused his tail, and returned to Sita. Showing her Rama's ring as proof that he was indeed his messenger, Hanuman reassured Sita that her husband would soon reach Lanka and slay Ravana. Then, taking from her a jewel that he could show Rama, he disappeared into the darkness of the night.

However, Sita's happiness after the encounter with Hanuman was short-lived. Agitated by a monkey's temerity to raze his palace to ashes, Ravana sent out his army of rakshasas to battle Rama's vanara sena or army of monkeys.

On the very first day of war, Ravana's son Indrajit bound Rama and Lakshmana with his Nagapasha, a noose made of live venomous snakes, causing the brothers to lose consciousness. Ravana immediately sent Sita with Trijata and other rakshasis to see the scene for herself, hoping she would finally believe that Rama was dead. However, Trijata realized that what they were seeing wasn't the complete truth.

'How can I believe that Rama is not dead?' Sita lamented as they flew across the battlefield in Ravana's Pushpaka Vimana. 'Look how still he lies, drawing not a single breath!'

Trijata smiled. Not only was Sita the most loving and faithful wife she had come across, she was also the most innocent; and it were these very qualities of hers that made Trijata want to take care of her. 'Don't grieve, Sita. You must believe me, for I know things that no one else does; I see things that no one else does,' she assured Sita.

Trijata was right. The venom from the snakes had paralysed Rama and Lakshmana, but they weren't dead yet. Even as the rakshasas celebrated their win, thousands of birds—eagles, hawks, kites and falcons—materialized from nowhere and ripped apart each and every snake that had wrapped itself around the bodies of Rama and Lakshmana; and as the sun rose on the battlefield the next morning, its every ray healed the brothers of their wounds and bruises. Soon, they were ready to fight again and this time, Lakshmana managed to kill Indrajit after a ferocious battle that lasted three days and three nights.

Trijata was the first to convey this news to Sita, who was overjoyed at first but then went back to doubting. 'The time has now come for Rama to confront Ravana. How will he be able to kill the invincible ten-headed rakshasa? We all know that he has the power to regrow his severed heads!'

Trijata closed her eyes for a while. When she opened them, she said, 'Don't worry, Sita. Ravana is destined to meet his end in the hands of Rama. Mark my words, Rama will shoot an arrow right through my Lord's heart; and although I will mourn the loss of my king, I will also rejoice Rama's victory, for I now know that he is the true king of the world.'

After the battle where Trijata's vision came true again,

Sita asked her to accompany her to Ayodhya. There, she was showered with many gifts for taking care of Sita like a true friend before she returned to Lanka.

Note

In Valmiki's Ramayana, Trijata is a wise, old rakshashi who makes her appearance only when Sita is brought to Ashoka Vatika. In later versions, though, Trijata has been referred to as Vibheeshana's daughter and hence, Ravana's niece. One version says that it was Vibheeshana who asked his daughter to be Sita's companion at Ashoka Vatika so that no harm came to her through Ravana or the other rakshasis. In most of these later versions, Trijata is shown to be wise, but not old.

16

Bhauma

It is said that when Vishnu, in the form of Varaha, had rescued Bhumi from the clutches of Hiranyaksha and restored her to her axis, a drop of his sweat fell on her. From this drop of sweat was born a child who grew up to terrorize the world. Who was he and how could he, the son of Vishnu, grow up to be a demon? Read on to find out.

Bhauma, named after his mother, Bhumi, was an intelligent and playful child. As he grew up, not only did he become stronger and more handsome but his intellect too multiplied manifold. Proud of her son, Bhumi asked Vishnu to give him the powerful weapon, Vaishnavastra.

'Be careful what you ask for, Bhumi,' Vishnu warned her. 'You love Bhauma because he is your son, but remember, he was born of me when I was in my Tamasic form—the form of an uncontrollable beast. He will grow up to be an asura and to arm an asura with such a powerful weapon would do great harm to the universe.'

Bhumi nodded. 'I understand, O Vishnu, but I also promise you this—my primary duty is to the millions of creations on earth, not to my child. If he ever resorts to evil deeds or turns destructive, I shall myself ensure his annihilation.'

Satisfied with Bhumi's vow, Vishnu gave Bhauma the weapon and disappeared. For several hundreds of years, Bhumi ensured that her son stayed in the path of righteousness. Bhauma established his kingdom at Pragjyotisha and ruled wisely from there. However, when another asura king, Bana, got wind of Bhauma's superior intellect, he wished to befriend him and make him an ally in his war against the devas.

Bana himself was extremely powerful. Being a staunch devotee of Shiva, he once used his thousand arms to play musical instruments when Shiva danced the Tandava Nritya. Pleased, Shiva granted him the boon that he himself would be the protector of Bana's kingdom. Thus, assured of his invincibility, Bana became increasingly cruel and arrogant. In his company, Bhauma too turned towards the vices and was soon eager to attack Devaloka.

'Bhauma, you are too innocent,' Bana laughed. 'You might be strong and intelligent, but that alone is not enough

to vanquish the devas for they have Vishnu's blessings. Go
forth and do some penance first. Pray to Brahma and ask him
for a boon that will make you invincible, like me...perhaps
immortal too.'

Thus, prodded by Bana, Bhauma left for the mountains,
where he prayed to Brahma for a thousand years. When
Brahma appeared before him to grant him a boon, Bhauma
cleverly decided not to ask for immortality. Instead, he said,
'O Brahma, grant me the boon of invincibility and if ever I have
to die, grant me that I shall die only at my mother's hands.'

Brahma smiled and granted him the boon and Bhauma
returned to his kingdom secure in the knowledge that his
loving mother would never kill him. Soon, in Bana's company,
he attacked Devaloka and driving the devas away, he occupied
Mani Parvata, the portion of the heavenly Mount Meru where
Indra usually spent his leisure time. His army looted Devaloka
and procured precious items such as Aditi's divine earrings
and Varuna's umbrella. However, Bhauma could still not find
contentment. Transforming himself into an elephant, he
kidnapped 16,000 beautiful maidens from both Devalok and
Bhuloka and imprisoned them in dungeons within the walls
of his impregnable fortress at Pragjyotisha.

Soon, there was chaos all over the universe. Sages and
their disciples scurried for cover as the asuras hindered
their sacrifices, kings and queens wailed as their daughters
disappeared one after the other, and the devas, hiding in the
caves of Mount Meru, worried whether their domain would
ever be restored to them.

When Bhumi became aware of the turmoil caused by

her son, she realized that the time had come to make good her promise to Vishnu. Incarnating herself as Satyabhama, she married Krishna and when Indra came to beseech her husband to vanquish Bhauma, she offered to go with him to battle the asura king.

Krishna and Satyabhama arrived at Pragjyotishpura, the capital of Pragjyotisha, on the back of Garuda. The city was well protected with several layers of obstacles. First lay an impenetrable barrier of magical mountains that would rise up from any side that an enemy tried to enter. Then came four formidable forts in each of the four directions followed by an invisible barricade of poisonous gases. Within it stood a fence made of tens of thousands of Mura-Pasha or strong noose-like ropes built by the demon Mura and finally, a moat filled with water in which Mura himself resided. Within it all, in the luxury of his palace, Bhauma sat smug in the knowledge that no one could breech the fortifications.

However, with the arrival of Krishna and Satyabhama, his peace was shattered by the sound of a conch shell that sent vibrations through the city.

'Who is it that dares to disturb the peace of my kingdom?' Bhauma thundered and sent his soldiers to investigate the intruder. They soon returned with disturbing news about Krishna's doings.

'O Lord, he sits with his wife on a giant bird and, with one swoop of his mace after another, he has destroyed all our defences—the entire range of magical mountains has been shattered, the poisonous gases are poisonous no more and the Mura-Pasha has come undone! But Lord, we still have hope for the sound of his conch has awoken the great Mura himself.'

Hearing the last few words, Bhauma smiled and forgot about the damage done by the intruder. Mura was his best warrior and he could rely on him to safeguard Pragjyotishpura.

Indeed, Mura was a demon as terrifying as could be. With five heads on a mountain-sized torso, his body emitted a dazzling brilliance against which even the sun paled; in the shroud of this brilliance, it was impossible to see him with open eyes. Asleep in the deep waters of the moat that surrounded the city, Mura woke up to the sound of Krishna's conch and sprung out in anger.

'Who dares disturb my sleep?' he demanded.

Then, looking at the destruction all around him, his eyes searched for the perpetrator. Spotting Garuda, he rushed towards the bird with his trident even as the thunderous roar emanating from his five mouths rumbled through the universe.

Seeing Mura approach, Krishna deftly threw two arrows towards the demon's trident, causing it to shatter to pieces. He then sent more arrows that pierced and lodged themselves into Mura's five mouths. Enraged at being out-manoeuvred, Mura threw his mace at Krishna. In retaliation, Krishna hurled his mace towards the approaching weapon and destroyed it before it could find its target.

Bereft of his weapon, Mura was on the brink of frustration when he remembered the boon he had been granted by Brahma after years of penance—that no one could kill him in physical combat. Mura smiled. He didn't need a weapon after all! Stretching himself so that his body towered over the city and hid the sun behind his gigantic frame, he charged at Krishna, hoping to crush him with his bare arms. However, before he could reach his rival, Krishna's Sudarshana Chakra came slicing through the air and separated his five heads from his body.

As Mura's mountain-like body slumped to the ground, a tremor shook the entire city of Pragjyotishpura. In his palace, Bhauma began to grow worried. Soon, his soldiers came and confirmed his worst fear—his valiant and trusted Mura was no more. But this wasn't the time to mourn; he immediately summoned the seven sons of Mura and said, 'Your father Mura has been mercilessly killed by an intruder. Go forth and avenge his death for that is your duty as his sons!'

Thus incited by Bhauma, Mura's sons—Tamra, Antariksha, Shranvana, Vibhavasu, Vasu, Nabhasvan and Aruna—stepped into the battlefield to face their father's killer under the leadership of General Pitha and Bhauma's eleven-akshouhini-strong army of asuras. In the ferocious fight that followed, they used weapons of all kinds—swords, spears, lances, maces and tridents—against Krishna, but each time, Krishna's arrows pierced the weapons and shattered them to pieces. Soon, Krishna had cut off the heads, arms, thighs and legs of Mura's sons and relegated them to the same fate as their father.

With all his commanders-in-chief dead, Bhauma decided to battle Krishna himself. Mounted on an elephant, he came out of the city gates to confront his enemy. Seeing Krishna and his wife seated on Garuda, he released Shatagni, a weapon that was capable of slaying several targets at one go. However, it was once again shattered to pieces with a single arrow shot by Krishna. Then, Garuda started to harass the horses and elephants on the battlefield by pecking at their bodies, causing them to retreat into the city in terror. Annoyed with his army being defeated by a wretched bird, Bhauma struck Garuda with his spear.

As a hurt Garuda fluttered, trying to maintain balance and protect Krishna and Satyabhama, Krishna conjured a chariot for himself and asked Satyabhama to become his charioteer. He then challenged his rival saying, 'O Bhauma, what a coward you are to choose to fight a bird rather than its master!'

Enraged by the taunt, Bhauma turned to face Krishna. In the ferocious fight that followed, he sent several magical weapons towards his rival, but Krishna destroyed all of them with his arrows until finally, Bhauma's spear struck Krishna on his head.

As Krishna fell unconscious on the battlefield, Satyabhama was furious. Picking up her husband's weapons, she continued to fight with Bhauma until finally, she sent the Sudarshana Chakra flying towards him and beheaded him.

Note

Bhauma is better known as Narakasura. In Hindu mythology, there are twenty-seven different kinds of hell, each having its own unique name such as Mahavicha, Amakumbha, Maharaurava, Mahatamisra and so on.

However, put together, they are known as 'Naraka'. It is said that this common name was derived from the acts of Naraka, whose tortures were synonymous with experiencing hell.

The day Naraka was slayed is celebrated as Naraka Chaturdashi. However, there are varying accounts of who killed the asura. While some texts attribute his killing to Krishna, others say it was Satyabhama and yet others claim it was Devi, in the form of Kali. However, all texts concur that Krishna killed the demon Mura and hence got the name 'Murari'.

There is a mention of the Vaishnavastra in the story. This was an extremely fast and powerful weapon that could be used to target an enemy by simply thinking of his name before firing it. Since the weapon was conjured by Vishnu himself, it could destroy any being but Vishnu or any of his incarnations. Although Bhauma did not know that Krishna was an incarnation of Vishnu, he, for some reason, did not use the Vaishnavastra against him. What happened to this potent weapon then? Well, after Bhauma's death, his son Bhagadatta inherited it and it is said that he tried using it against Arjuna in the great battle of Kurukshetra. However, Krishna, knowing the destructive power of the weapon, rose from the charioteer's seat to obstruct the path of the Vaishnavastra and protect Arjuna. As soon as the weapon touched Krishna's chest, it is said to have transformed into a garland of flowers, having gone back to its original owner.

17

Jvara

When Krishna's grandson Aniruddha eloped with Usha, the daughter of the daitya king Bana, with the intention of marrying her, Bana was enraged. He immediately gathered an army of asuras and declared war on Aniruddha. In the battle that followed, Aniruddha defeated Bana but the latter, not able to withstand the humiliation, used his powers of illusion to bind his rival with a cord of venomous snakes and made him prisoner. This act naturally angered Krishna, who set off to Sonitpura, the capital of Bana's kingdom, along with Balarama and a large Yadava army. In the course of the fierce battle that followed, Krishna and Balarama came face to face with a demon with three legs, three heads, six arms and nine eyes. Who was this demon? Let's discover.

✧

Once, Shiva was deep in meditation at his abode in Kailasa when a drop of sweat formed on his forehead. Out of this was born Jvarasura, a fever-causing demon, who soon spread his terror across the three worlds. Approached by the devas and rishis to end the destruction caused by him, Vishnu, in the form of Hayagriva, fought a fierce battle against Jvara and killed him by cutting him into three pieces with the Sudarshana Chakra.

Brahma wasn't pleased with Jvara's death though. The latter was the companion of Shitala, Brahma's daughter, who had emerged from the sacrificial fire as the one who would both cause and cure all diseases. Hoping to placate his despairing daughter, Brahma set out to bring together the parts of Jvara's body in order to join them. However, even before he could collect them, each of the three parts magically sprouted a three-eyed head, a leg and two arms of its own. So, when Brahma finally joined them and breathed life into the body, the demon thus reborn had three heads, three legs, six arms and nine eyes. The new Jvara also had the remarkable ability to move in several directions at the same time!

Brahma then sent Shitala and Jvara to Bhuloka, where they lived amongst humans and animals for several hundred years, until Krishna declared war on Bana.

Years ago, Bana, the son of the daitya King Mahabali and a devotee of Shiva, had played the mridangam with his thousand arms as his Lord performed the Tandava

Nritya. Pleased, Shiva granted him the boon that he would always protect Bana's kingdom from enemies. Now, as Bana prepared to face Krishna's army in battle, Shiva sent forth Kartikeya, along with all his ganas to help Bana defend himself. Jvara, being the son of Shiva, was also part of this ferocious army.

As the battle commenced, the ganas and the asura army attacked the Yadava army but, with Garuda, Balarama and Krishna on their side, the latter soon sent the asuras running for cover. Seeing the retreating asura army, Jvara roared like a storm. He then strode into the battlefield, his demonic form, fiery eyes and repeated thunderous sighs and yawns evoking fear and dread amongst his rivals. With ashes as his weapon, he looked like Yama, the God of Death himself, as he went towards Balarama.

'O wielder of the plough, do you think your strength can match mine? Mark my words, you will not escape this battle alive...it is only a matter of time before you are dead!' So saying, Jvara adopted a thousand different forms and whirled all around his rival in such a short span of time that Balarama was left perplexed.

Jvara then flung blazing ashes towards Balarama. As soon as they hit Balarama's mountain-like body, the ashes bounced and fell on Mount Meru, shattering its peak. However, some of the ash clung on to his chest and soon, Balarama was being consumed by it—he began to yawn and sigh repeatedly, his body hair stood erect, his eyes dilated and his vision began to fade. He was soon moving about recklessly. Maddened by the terrifying blaze that was pushing him towards unconsciousness, he cried out to Krishna. 'O Krishna, my body is burning all over and I can bear it no more! I am being consumed. Tell me, how can I be saved?'

Seeing his elder brother's plight, Krishna ran to his side and lovingly embraced him. Almost immediately, the heat dissipated from Balarama's body; he was rescued from the jaws of death.

Then, enraged at the suffering caused to his brother, Krishna said, 'O Jvara, come and fight me. Show me the extent of your power and strength in this great battle!'

Jvara too was infuriated that Balarama had escaped death. With two of his right hands, he flung the blazing ashes towards Krishna. When the ashes touched his body, Krishna experienced a burning sensation for an instant, but before Jvara had a reason to rejoice, the fire died on its own. Incensed, Jvara first struck Krishna on his neck with his serpent-like long arms and then dealt a blow on his chest. Krishna retaliated by striking Jvara with his hands.

During the terrifying duel that followed, a thunderous roar descended on the mountains. Jvara used his powers of magic to fly into the sky but was soon overpowered by Krishna, who brought him down and crushed him with his arms. Then, just when Krishna thought that he had killed Jvara, the latter, freed from the brutal clutches of his rival, entered his body. Thus possessed by the fever demon, Krishna felt all energy draining from his body. His movement slackened and he tottered on the battlefield, repeatedly seeking the support of the ground. Even as the Yadava army watched on, he let out a yawn and was soon overcome with sleep.

Jvara was pleased with himself and let out a thunderous laugh. However, his joy was short-lived for Krishna soon realized the reason for his devastating weakness. To counter his rival, Krishna created another Jvara, as potent and dreadful as the original Jvara, through his power of meditation. Almost immediately, the fever demon was pushed out of Krishna's body. With his infinite strength and power restored, a furious Krishna struck Jvara down and was about to tear him to pieces when a voice from the skies asked him to show mercy. Jvara too realized that his rival was no ordinary warrior. He bowed down before Krishna and asked to be pardoned.

'O Jvara, you were only doing your duty and for that, you must be praised. Since you have realized your folly, I shall protect you and grant you a boon. Tell me, what do you desire?'

'O Krishna, let it be then that I am the only Jvara in this universe, that no one else similar to me may flourish.'

'So be it,' replied Krishna. 'The Jvara of my creation will merge back into me and you shall be the only Jvara as before! However, you must now listen to my command. If you truly seek to please me, divide yourself into three parts—with one part, you shall possess four-legged animals, with the second, you shall possess the immobile world of trees, lands and mountains, and with the third, you shall live in the midst of humans and birds. In the trees, you shall be the insect that feeds on them and the disease that withers up the leaves and rots the fruits. In flowers, you shall be the frost; on earth, you shall be the desert and in water, you shall be the plant that spreads itself like a parasite. Thus, you shall pervade the entire Bhuloka and with your very view or touch, all lives, except those of humans and gods, will perish.'

Upon hearing Krishna's words, Jvara was delighted. 'O Krishna, you have won me over with your compassion. I shall do as you command and in return let it be that whenever a human afflicted by me reads this account of our fight, he shall be relieved of his disease!' So saying, Jvara retreated from the battle once and for all.

Note

The battle raged on after Jvara retreated and when Bana finally arrived at the battlefield to confront Krishna, the latter trounced him and cut off all his arms except two. He spared Bana's life at the request of Shiva; Bana in turn apologized for his actions and gave his consent for the marriage of Aniruddha and Usha.

Note from the Author

When reading some of the stories in the book, you might have come across gods and demons fighting continuously for thousands of years or asuras doing penance for hundreds and thousands of years. Similarly, there are stories where the gods or asuras can expand themselves to cover several kilometres or sometimes, the entire expanse of the earth or sky. Did they strike you as being odd? They sure left me perplexed when I first came across them while doing my research. How can someone, however powerful or strong-willed he is, manage to sustain a fight or a prayer for such a long time? How can someone become so unbelievably gigantic? Curious, I went back to read up on the concept of time and space in Hindu mythology and this is what I found...

... but before I start, you might want to run and get yourself a calculator. What? A calculator for a book on demons and demonesses? Well, read along and find out why and if you've been too lazy to get out of your couch, don't complain that you weren't warned!

Let's first look at space. In Vedic times, the basis of measuring distances or sizes was the average height of a human (nara), which was roughly 5.3 feet. So, when we talk about a 'yojana', it is essentially 8,000 humans long or 42,400 feet. Converting this into kilometres, we get a length of roughly 13 kilometres. Remember, Mount Meru mentioned earlier in the book? According to the Puranas, the mountain, said to be made of solid gold, spans a height of 84,000 yojanas of which, 16,000 yojanas are below the earth. It is said to be 32,000 yojanas wide at its summit and 16,000 yojanas wide at its foot. Some quick calculation (ok...not so quick!) will tell you that the mountain was roughly 10,92,000 kilometres tall. Compare this to the distance between the earth and the moon—a meagre 3,84,000 kilometres. Mind-boggling, right? No wonder Meru was called the King of Mountains!

Coming to the story of Madhu and Kaitabha, we read that 'the demons also enlarged their bodies to the extent of a thousand yojanas'; it meant that they expanded their bodies to cover a distance of 13,000 kilometres, which is essentially the diameter of the earth! Now you know why the earth trembled and ocean waters rose to unrealistic heights when a demon like Hiranyaksha, whose crown touched the sky, walked! Similarly, Varaha grew from a tiny boar to one that was 6,000 yojanas in height. Why don't you do the calculation this time and find out just how tall he was?

Now that you've got a fair idea of sizes in the realm of gods, let us look at the idea of time. Hinduism believes in a cyclical concept of time which means, there is no single start or end to the universe—when the universe, as we know it, self-destructs at the end of a hundred Brahma years, a new universe is automatically born with a new Brahma (creator) and continues for another hundred Brahma years. But hey, what is a Brahma year?

You will be surprised to know that a whole year in the human world constitutes a single day in the realm of the devas, with half a year making up their day time and the other half making up their night time. With a little bit of math, we can calculate that one deva year comes to 365 (approximated to 360) human years. So, while we consider it an achievement or miracle when a human completes a hundred years, you can be sure the devas are pooh-poohing us from their abode, for they can live up to 4.32 million human years! These crazy number of years roughly translate into 12,000 deva years or a Maha Yuga, which comprises four smaller yugas: Satya Yuga that spans 4,800 deva years, Treta Yuga that is made up of 3,600 deva years, Dwapara Yuga that is made up of 2,400 deva years and finally Kali Yuga that comprises 1,200 deva years. Thus, the Kali Yuga (the yuga that we are believed to be living in) can be calculated to be 4,32,000 human years (1,200 x 360 human years).

As per calculations by scholars, twenty-seven Maha Yugas have passed since this universe of ours was created. We live in the Kali Yuga portion of the twenty-eighth Maha Yuga and believe it or not, only around 5,100 years have passed out of the 4,32,000 years that comprise this yuga!

Coming to the gods, since they are above the devas in

hierarchy, their measure of time should be different too, shouldn't it? So, if one human year equals a single day for the devas, a thousand Maha Yugas (1,000 x 4.32 million human years) equals just half a day in the life of Brahma! If you're not a fan of math, I can totally understand if your head starts spinning right at this moment...but I have to complete this mind-boggling calculation, so bear with me. Coming back to Brahma, a single day in his life is made up of 8,640,000,000 (8.6 billion) human years and 360 such years constitute one Brahma year. According to one version of the story behind the creation of the universe, the gods live on for a hundred Brahma years, at the end of which they dissolve into nothingness before the next cycle of life starts afresh. Another version says that a hundred Brahma years represent a single breath of Mahavishnu. When Mahavishnu inhales, the entire universe is destroyed and merges with his body; when he exhales, the universe is recreated anew!

To put things in the perspective of demons and demonesses, since they are our focus in this book, many asuras and rakshasas lived for thousands and thousands of human years, but never for 12,000 deva years. So, when they performed their extreme penances and asked Brahma for immortality, they were essentially asking him the boon that they too could continue living for 4.32 million human years!

Do you want to live that long? Well, to start with, you could try standing on one leg, arms stretched above your head and meditate without food or water for at least a day... what say?

Acknowledgements

In researching for this book, I have referred to English translations of a multitude of texts including relevant chapters/portions from the *Rig Veda, Satapatha Brahmana, Atharva Veda, Bhagavata Purana, Harivamsam, Shiva Purana, Devi Bhagawata Purana, Skanda Purana, Markandeya Purana, Vishnu Purana, Vamana Purana, Padma Purana, Valmiki Ramayana, Ramcharitmanas* and *Srimad Bagawatham*. I have also referred to some important works by known Indophiles and scholars of Hindu mythology who have left me humbled, given the sheer depth and passion reflected in their research. While their books have been mentioned in the bibliography at the end of the book, here, I would like to acknowledge their invaluable contribution in helping me better understand the various strands that tie this book together.

The internet has been a constant companion through this journey as I browsed several websites and blogs to dig for lesser-known details of some stories. While I'll run out of space if I start listing them here, I would like to acknowledge their collective contribution to this book. I do, of course, realize that one cannot blindly accept what one finds on the internet as the truth; consequently, I have taken care to authenticate all the information so gathered before using them in my stories.

I would like to thank my grandmothers, both of whom are in their nineties, and my aunt, Narayani, who, with their immense inherited wisdom, helped me choose and present here, the appropriate version of some of the stories. My thanks also to Appa, my sister and brother-in-law and my husband, for being my silent supporters, always, and my lovable nephews, who qualify to be devas in every way.

I can't thank my two children enough for not only being my beta-readers and first critics but also occasionally demonstrating the ways of the asuras and rakshasas with their ferocious fights in the battlefield called home! And, I must admit, for silently suffering the many asura stories I've conjured during this journey, including Pandasura and the Dragon Gods—the outcome of my son snuggling next to me in anticipation of a fantastic bed-time story and my eyes falling on a tiny Panda toy that graces a wall in my room.

A big thank you to Saswati, my editor, for coming to me with this amazing concept that opened the doors for a fantastic journey through space and time that I'd otherwise have never embarked upon.

The primary source for most stories in the book is my mother, whom I won't thank, because you don't thank mothers...you just love them.

Bibliography

A Prose English Translation of Harivamsha: Translated Literally into English Prose. (1897). India: H.C. Dass, Elysium Press.

Dalal, R. (2014). *Hinduism: An Alphabetical Guide*. India: Penguin Books Limited.

Debroy, B. (2016). *Harivamsha*. India: Penguin Books Limited.

Doniger, W. (1980). *The Origins of Evil in Hindu Mythology*. United States: University of California Press.

Gopinatha Rao, T.A. (1985). *Elements of Hindu Iconography*. India: Motilal Banarsidass.

Hale, W. (1999). *Ásura in Early Vedic Religion*. India: Motilal Banarsidass.

Kak, S. (2000). *The Astronomical Code of the Ṛgveda*. India: Munshiram Manoharlal Publishers.

Krishna, N. (2007). *The Book of Demons*. India: Penguin Books Limited.

Sattar, A. (2016). *Uttara: The Book of Answers*. India: Penguin Books Limited.

Śrīmad Bhāgavatam: With the Original Sanskrit Text, its Roman Transliteration, Synonyms, Translation and Elaborate Purports. (1999). India: Bhaktivedanta Book Trust.

Thompson, R.L. (1989). *Vedic Cosmography and Astronomy*. United States: Bhaktivedanta Book Trust.

Wilkins, W. (1973). *Hindu Mythology, Vedic and Purānic. 2nd ed*. Curzon Press.